INTERACTIVITY

INTERACTIVITY

DESIGNING AND USING INTERACTIVE VIDEO

Michael Picciotto, Ian Robertson and Ray Colley

KOGAN
PAGE

First published in 1989 by
Kogan Page Ltd,
120 Pentonville Road, London N1 9JN

British Library Cataloguing in Publication Data

Picciotto, Michael
   Interactivity: designing and using
   interactive video
   1. Great Britain. Personnel. Training.
   Applications of interactive video systems
   I. Title   II. Robertson, Ian
   III. Colley, Ray
   658.3'24
   ISBN 1-85091-587-3

Printed and bound in Great Britain by
Billings & Sons Ltd, Worcester

CONTENTS

FOREWORD

During the last few years in the UK a number of brave spirits have set out to make interactive video for educational purposes. They have been working mostly in advance of serious knowledge of the potential for using IV in education and have had to make up many of the ground rules and set directions as they progressed. No doubt design principles for educational interactive video will be increasingly widely understood and a grammar will emerge; but those who begin in the future to design with confidence will owe a debt of gratitude to the pioneers.

Of course the essence of pioneering is that one is so busy driving it that there is no time to leave proper marks for others to follow — the odd slash on a tree here, an occasional bent piece of grass there. This book sets out to tell the story of one such journey in detail. The authors have taken a great deal of trouble to document their path. I hope those who follow will find this a useful and practical guide.

Angus Doulton
Director
National Interactive Video Centre
January 1989

Chapter 1

WHAT IS INTERACTIVE VIDEO?

INTRODUCTION

Interactive video (IV) is not new: in various forms it has been in existence for more than a decade. It is, however, little known in training and education and there are question marks over its every aspect: hardware, software, video resources, content, appropriate use and, indeed, the very nature of the medium.

In case this seems unnecessarily forbidding as an introduction, let us quickly say that it is very easy to supply a simple and straightforward definition of IV: it is essentially the result of linking the power of the computer to a video playback facility of some kind. Both of these media are well known for supplying powerful and motivating training experiences. IV allows a fusion of the interactive possibilities provided by the computer and the visual impact of the video.

IV as Hardware

In hardware terms, IV involves the linking of a videotape or videodisc player with some form of computer processing power. The output of the system is shown on one or more screens. Where one screen only is used, the system must contain some form of interface allowing the display of computer and video output on the single screen, and the screen itself must be capable of displaying both forms of output.

IV as a Medium

Describing IV in simply hardware terms is a little like describing television without discussing programme making and content. It is still common for hardware issues to dominate discussions at conferences and exhibitions dealing with IV. What is more, technical developments have outstripped by far the general understanding of IV as a medium and the average level of creativity shown in implementing courseware.

There w ll be more discussion later as to the nature of IV. At this stage it is sufficient to say that a n IV programme uses the configuration to deliver training or information. The video source provides high quality video and audio as its component, and the computer allows interaction by and with the user. Either the computer program initiates a response from the user or the user requests a response from the computer program. In turn, the software can use the video source to provide part or all of this response. The most direct form of this kind of interaction is the arcade game which uses video rather than computer graphics. To give the general idea, one such game is a standard 'shoot-em-up' arcade game which differs from the norm by using flying sequences from a feature film . The user manoeuvres the aircraft and presses the trigger; the software determines whether or not the aim is true, amends the score accordingly and gives feedback in the form of appropriate video sequences.

The two features which are said to characterize interactive video are random access and branching. Random access is the ability of a videodisc player to select and play any part of a videodisc in any order.

Branching makes use of this random access capability to allow users to follow different paths through programmes according to their particular needs or responses. What makes IV come to life as a medium is the design of content and software — what the programme does and how it does it.

As we have seen, IV can be viewed and described in different ways. It is a hardware combination, a type of courseware, a fusion of media or a hybrid technology. Because expertise from a number of highly specialized fields is needed to implement an IV programme there is a good deal of controversy among practitioners as to the nature of the medium, the working practices required for successful implementations and the appropriate blend of qualifications and experience desirable in the IV project team.

About this Book

This book is intended to address a number of key issues in IV and to serve as a guide at various levels. We hope that it will prove useful in the following ways:

Basic Level

(a) As an introduction to the basic vocabulary and concepts of IV.

(b) As a source of information to trainers who wish to gain some understanding of the technology and why it is regarded as potentially so important.

(c) To help you to decide whether IV is a suitable answer to your general or specific training needs.

Intermediate Level

(a) As a guide to various ways of gaining entry to the medium.

(b) As a way of stimulating thought and suggesting possible applications.

Advanced Level

(a) To supply the knowledge required to implement a project.

(b) To supply experienced insights into the nature of the medium and its potential.

We shall try to do these things in four ways: by describing the capabilities of the medium and the tools it affords; by describing characteristic uses of the medium; by using a case study of the stages of implementation of an actual advanced IV application, and by reporting our views and thoughts about suitable and appropriate implementation methods, configurations and uses for interactive media now and in the future.

We also wish to challenge some of the assumptions which are made about the nature of IV; assumptions which we feel are impeding its development. It seems odd to talk about traditional views in a relatively young technology, yet there already seem to be a number of perceptions about the "correct" design of IV courseware and the features necessary to dignify it with the adjective interactive.

The Authors

Two of the authors gained their experience in IV working on a research and development project dealing with an application of interactive video to foreign language learning. This applications area is considered one of the most difficult for computer-based training techniques and the completed project represents a convincing solution to some very intractable problems. The finished courseware has enjoyed a very warm reception from the training, IV, education and industrial communities.

The third author who has provided the video expertise was formerly BBC regional TV manager, Manchester, and has been responsible for the production of many hundreds of hours of BBC television programmes over a period of 25 years.

THE APPLICATIONS

In-House, Commissioned, and Generic Applications

IV applications are often referred to as in-house, commissioned or generic.

In-house programmes, including video production, instructional design, subject expertise and software are produced entirely by the organization wishing to use them. This approach is often adopted by large companies, particularly if there is an important element of confidentiality in the content of the package or if the organization considers its needs to be very specific.

Commissioned programmes usually make use of an organization's subject expertise, but call on the IV skills of an outside organization or organizations to implement different elements of the programme.

Generic applications are the IV world's equivalent of publishing: they are programmes which deal with requirements common to a number of organizations. They are implemented by IV producers and intended for the general market. Organizations involved in the sale of generic courseware have often tended to concentrate on customer handling and business management skills. Some IV producers in this part of the market lease hardware and courseware to companies wishing to use IV without committing themselves to buying hardware.

These three categories are not completely separate. Often productions are partly in-house but buy in specific areas of expertise or facilities, such as video production or software. There are also organizations which adapt the videodiscs provided as part of a generic package by bolting on alternative instructional design and software.

Areas of application

IV is currently used in the following areas:

- Training and Education
- Point of Sale
- Public Information
- Archiving
- Leisure

Training and Education

Training currently accounts for well over half of the total number of IV applications in use in the UK.

For educational and training purposes the most commonly understood ways of using the technology involve a 'branching' or problem-solving approach. As in a computer simulation, users can be presented with scenarios and choices leading to various 'branching' paths through a learning programme. In this way it is possible to present users with a follow-up scenario which illustrates the consequences of decisions taken.

Possibly the most dramatic programme of this type is the cardiopulmonary resuscitation programme commissioned by the American Heart Association. In this system, the life-size dummy which is part of the IV workstation responds to the learner's efforts to revive the 'patient'. If the learner applies the wrong technique, the dummy 'dies.'

Although IV cannot improve on real-life experience, it can be used where it would be too difficult, dangerous or costly to provide the real thing. It would be unrealistic, for example, to lay on a genuine oil rig fire to train specialist fire-fighters. In skills training, the breakdown is usually between 'hard skills' — things such as operating procedures for machinery and 'soft skills' — negotiation, management, decision-making and communications. In soft skills training there are no black and white answers and a well designed IV programme can provide realistically graded outcomes.

Point of Sale

Point of sale applications aim to provide promotional information on site in retail outlets. Compared to the continuous video presentations which run in some stores, IV point of sale systems are much more likely to involve potential customers through drawing them into interaction. They are able to respond to a customer's specific needs rather than give a generalized and uninterruptable presentation, they can give a much more comprehensive catalogue of available goods, and they can easily be updated with information on prices and availability by altering the data held in the computer.

Public Information

Public information programmes differ from point of sale mostly in intention rather than style, as they do not attempt to sell products. Often the clear aim of such systems is public relations, and it may be that concept or image is subtly sold by information system. This is particularly true where the medium is used to inform or influence the public in areas where 'boring but essential' public information or unpopular industries are concerned.

Archiving

Archiving and the use of pictorial/computer databases can often be much more dynamic than the name suggests. Perhaps the best known IV archive is the BBC/ Acorn/Philips Domesday Project. The Domesday package is being energetically promoted to education as an exploratory resource which can be used across wide areas of the curriculum. It is also proving attractive to companies in the private sector with a need for flexible and speedy access to topographical information.

An Overview of Interactive Video Applications

The following brief skim through a number of IV applications in the United States, the UK and Europe describes market sectors which are using IV and how they are using it. This should help you to think about what type of application is best suited to your needs.

Computer Industry
(a) United States
As you would expect, the computer industry in the United States was the first and most notable sector to exploit IV. The applications in the industry tend to focus on customer and staff training and on point of sale or information systems.

IBM have traditionally put a great deal of emphasis on training for company personnel, dealers and customers. Each of the 150 IBM Guided Learning Centers in American cities has several interactive video self-learning stations. Considerable savings in personnel costs are reported. There are estimated to be 3000 workstations in existence which are designed for computer training and sales promotion.

Digital Equipment Corporation (DEC) markets a system known as IVIS (Interactive Video Information System) and there are currently 2000 workstations in use. DEC reports a reduction in training time of between 23 per cent and 46 per cent compared to other self-teaching methods. In 1987 three quarters of all DEC's service training programmes were expected to use IVIS in 515 training stations worldwide. The annual savings are expected to run into millions of dollars.

Other computer companies using interactive video for training and sales promotion include Wang, Hewlett-Packard, NCR, Control Data Corporation and Apple.
(b) Europe
IBM in Europe has also made very large scale use of IV for sales support and training of technical staff and dealers. These facilities are notably in use in the UK and West Germany.

Also in West Germany, Nixdorf and Siemens use IV for information delivery and training.

Military

Military applications are particularly appropriate for interactive video Many military training applications, such as weapons training, involve extremely high costs or potentially dangerous situations, for example, where actual firing of weapons is required.

(a) United States

The US Army has long experience in the use of IV self-training stations, including use by American forces in Europe, at the US Army Defense School at Fort Bliss in Texas and at the US Army Signal School.

An evaluation of the statistics reported from various locations and measured against conventional training methods gave very positive results.

- Average concentration spans increased by over 250 per cent.
- Average reduction in problem solution times 49 per cent
- Reduction in course costs from $120m to $1.7m

It is projected that by 1990 the US Army will have spent approximately half a billion dollars on 47,000 interactive video training stations

The US Air Force has a language training centre which is installing multi-media self-teaching stations. The language training delivered is based firmly on the use of authored IV programmes driving dedicated videodiscs. The language instructors in the centre are generally drawn from the mainstream of Air Force personnel judged to have sufficient language skills rather than specialist language teachers. Training in courseware design and language teaching methodology is usually given after staff join the centre. It is clear that in such circumstances, the reliability of training which can be delivered by an IV system is highly desirable.

One interesting application commissioned by the US Navy illustrates the dual purpose potential of many IV projects. The Navy has a videodisc holding all known ship silhouettes of all nations. It is easy to classify this as a classic pictorial database application, but in this case the principal use of the database is in training submarine crews.

(b) Europe

In the UK there exist a number of military applications of IV, mostly again for training purposes, including training for fitters and mechanics on Chieftain tanks, air-to-air refuelling, driver training and gunnery.

Another programme, *Navyfax*, produced for the Royal Navy by the Central Office of Information, illustrates another possible application of the point of sale application, in this case designed for recruiting purposes.

Applications in West Germany include programmes designed for the training of pilots, guided missile operators and maintenance personnel. IV is used in France for training of tank crews and in Switzerland for training members of the civil defence organization.

Car Industry

(a) United States

Companies such as General Motors, Ford, American Motors and Toyota all have a large installed base of videodisc players and applications, many of them in car showrooms. These are generally used for product demonstrations, and explanations of cars and trucks for potential customers.

Some companies have gone further afield in their attempts to reach possible customers and have installed product information systems in airports and other areas heavily used by the general public. Although the intention of such systems places them firmly in the point of sale category, their actual siting makes a description of sales promotion more accurate. A number of companies have also found that videodiscs containing customer information can be used with different software as a resource for the training of sales staff and other employees.

One very large chain of motor spares retailers has 115 'Video-Tech Centres' in its stores to provide DIY information available to shoppers. There are currently believed to be a minimum of 18,000 videodisc players or full IV systems in use in the American motor industry.

(b) Europe

The picture in Europe is quite consistent with American developments, with car manufacturers among the largest users of IV for training and sales promotion.

The applications mostly break down into technical training, sales training and customer information, with individual companies showing a clear preference for particular applications.

In the UK, Jaguar have largely seen IV as a medium for the delivery of technical training; while Austin Rover's uses of IV have centred on the provision of training for sales staff, managers and supervisors. Vauxhall and Volvo have mostly used it for customer information

In Europe, Volkswagen and Audi have sales promotion applications. Fiat have employed mixed applications across training, sales and customer information and Daimler-Benz and BMW have commissioned exhibition information systems.

Medicine and Health
(a) United States

There are a great many IV applications in these fields in the United States. They include training programmes and aids to diagnosis for doctors, as well as public and patient awareness and education programmes.

The number of IV applications in this area tends to highlight many of its advantages. As a delivery medium for training, IV permits access to the delicate combination of personal qualities and professional expertise required by the medical profession. For patient awareness, on the other hand, the non-threatening responses of an IV system can be very effective in overcoming fear of taking medical advice. This can be particularly beneficial for sensitive topics such as AIDS education.

(b) Europe

In Europe similarly, many medical training and awareness programmes exist. Most of the training applications are aimed at doctors, with some targeting nurses, and there is a small overlap into sales promotion with those applications which are aimed at training pharmaceutical industry representatives.

Health education programmes include the Health Education Council's '*Thinking about Drinking*' in the UK; the Haefner Verlag '*Mutter und Kind*' and the associated

Bounty Vision information programmes for young mothers in West Germany and the UK and the '*Eat Right — Eat Well* ' programme developed by the Co-op in the UK.

Training applications for medicine often employ case-study and simulation techniques in programme such as those developed by Smith Kline and French Labs Ltd. Titles include '*And the BP's up a bit too*', '*Patient Management Simulation: Mike Roberts*' and '*Mary Weatherton: The British contribution to diagnostic challenge*'

Not all applications in the medical field concentrate on high level professional skills: Middlesex Hospital Medical School has had support from the Department of Trade and Industry to develop '*Back to Basics*', an IV programme designed to train hospital staff in correct techniques for lifting patients.

It is useful also to mention the archival discs produced by the University of London Audiovisual Centre: '*The Inguinal Region*' and '*The Knee*', and Longman/Grollier's '*Body Disc*'.

Commercial
(a) United States
Commercial use of IV systems can be found in all kinds of retail outlets including DIY shops, garden centres, photographic dealers, furniture shops, baby goods stores, shoe shops, fashion shops and even art galleries. Generally videodiscs are used in customer self-service information kiosks.

A system installed by Cuisinarts gives gift tips, prints out recipes and makes shopping lists. Some point of sale systems even allow direct ordering through the systems. One major shoe store reports an increase in sales of 15 per cent with their IV point of sale system.

A study by LINK resources has estimated 8200 videodisc based customer self-service information kiosks in the USA in 1986, 12 per cent of which are linked to data banks. By 1990 this is projected to have risen to 113 000 systems, 42 per cent of which will be linked to data banks.

The flexibility of IV is demonstrated by Revco, the largest American drug store chain. It has a system which gives information on health and beauty issues including eye and skin care, the correct use of vitamins, fitness training and treatment of diabetes. These 'Better Health Information Center' kiosks are clearly intended as sales promotion, but may also be regarded as a public health information facility.

(b) Europe
In Europe, many IV companies have produced discs or packages designed to show off the medium itself or present its facilities. These include demonstration discs by Philips, Eindhoven, Visage, the Moving Picture Company, Convergent Communications, Sprint and Videodem.

Perhaps the best known UK point of sale application is the Mothercare system which was trialled in four branches. The average increase in sales over a period of six months was over 20 per cent. More recently, Littlewoods PLC have been piloting their Littlewoods Instant Shopping Adviser (LISA). As often happens with this kind of system, the resources of the videodisc have also been exploited to provide training modules for shop staff. Asda have also tested a point of sale programme about vacuum cleaners and report a sales increase of 45 per cent.

The dual purpose commercial and training use of the same disc can be seen in other organizations such as British Telecom

Banks, Finance and Insurance
a) United States
IV use by banks usually falls into two categories: training for bank staff and customer information.

Many banks use IV to train staff, particularly counter staff in customer handling skills. These may range from telephone skills through ways of putting customers at ease to techniques for recognizing and exploiting opportunities to sell bank services.

The area of public information in banks and financial institutions may also be regarded as one where customers may be nervous of speaking to an assistant and may feel more prepared to browse through available services using a non- threatening IV system. In all of these public and customer information applications, IV systems are assuming a role which has classically been regarded as appropriate for computer power: dealing very efficiently with predictable routine work — in this case responding to the commonest customer enquiries —while freeing human resources to deal with situations which are best handled by human beings.

(b) Europe
In the UK banks have been amongst the most enthusiastic users of IV. The largest user is Lloyd's Bank which in 1986 installed 1500 IV workstations for staff training at a cost of £6 m.

This organization's involvement in IV has been progressive, with the earliest programmes commissioned from IV production companies, and later ones being increasingly produced in house as experience has grown.

The National Westminster Bank has also made use of training ('Smile, you're on the telephone') and point of sale programmes, as has the Midland Bank and a number of building societies and insurance companies.

Prominent among generic programme producers are Financial i Ltd, who have specialized in financial training for bankers and accountants. It is also interesting to mention the programme produced by the Industrial Development Board of Northern Ireland which is intended to promote investment in Northern Ireland from Japanese sources.

A common theme in this sector of IV applications is the perception that financial information and training is normally seen as indigestible and boring and that IV can improve interest and motivation.

Tourism and Hotels
a) United States
This is a field which would seem to be tailor-made for a data-retrieval pictorial database application. In the tourism industry there is clearly a need for a system which can offer on-line information in an appealing form. The industry spends a great deal of money on illustrated catalogues of holiday destinations and resorts: interactive pictorial data banks could provide information in a very appealing format to prospective holidaymakers.

Information systems have currently been installed by American Express, Motourist Info Centers and Amtrak. These offer variously an advisory booking system in travel agencies with a data bank link; information systems at highway fuel stations and motels with tourist attractions, hotels and restaurants; and city tourist information and tourism advertising at railway stations.

Sheraton Hotels have also installed a videodisc- supported automatic check-in check-out system. The reported benefits are much reduced costs and greatly improved speed and efficiency for guests checking in and out. As in the banking applications above, the system can cope with and improve routine service requirements, thus giving hotel staff more time to provide good personal service.

(b) Europe

In Europe information systems have been produced for the Loire Regional Tourist Information Board, the Black Forest Tourist Information Board, the British Tourist Authority, English Tourist Board and even the South Lakeland District Council. As in the United States, training programmes centre on the hotel industry — mostly customer handling skills — and the travel industry.

Museums and Public Information

(a) United States

Museums in the United States employing IV public information systems for visitors include the Museum of Modern Art, the National Air and Space Museum and the National Gallery of Art.

In the Museum of Modern Art there are self-service information systems in each exhibition room which describe the exhibits in the museum and classify them into periods.

The National Air and Space Museum has 10 000 still photographs of aircraft from archives stored on videodisc, which can be accessed by museum visitors. The discs can also be purchased by visitors. This is a theme common to the system at the National Gallery of Art where 1645 slides and films of all museum exhibits are stored and available from videodisc. The disc can also be used for a guided tour of the museum. Here again, as well as calling up the disc in exhibition rooms, visitors can buy it for $95.

These last two applications offer an interesting insight into videodisc costs, which are often assumed to be very high: the 1645 stills of the National Gallery of Art disc would cost $4000 if bought as individual slides. It is likely that the 10 000 stills on the Air and Space Museum disc would cost well over $15000 bought separately.

Other places with installed public information systems include Disneyland and the EPCOT Center and a number of national parks.

(b) Europe

Museums in Europe and Scandinavia using IV information booths include the Geological Museum in London, the Musée de la Villette in Paris, the National French Army Museum and the Norwegian Museum of Science and Industry in Oslo.

One area of public information which has been frequently explored by European IV information systems has been that of employment and welfare. Packages of this type include programmes produced for the Manpower Services Commission in the UK to give employment information in job centres.

A number of organizations, including ICI, General Motors UK, Westland Helicopters, the Milton Keynes Development Corporation, the Saudi-Arabian Ministry of

Information and the Museum of Mankind have made use of the medium to provide eye-catching demonstrations and displays for exhibitions.

The Armargh Planetarium should be mentioned here. It is difficult to decide how exactly to classify the project, but superbly imaginative work has been done here using videodiscs, including elements of education, entertainment and public information.

Effectively, by using handsets to register choices, the Planetarium provides in its '*Odyssey*' the opportunity for the audience to control its own show. Audience majority responses automatically activate the star theatre equipment in an interactive exploration of the Sun, planets and minor bodies.

Point of information programmes can sometimes be rather more precisely targeted, as with British Steel's 'Nerves of Steel' which is designed to stimulate graduate recruitment to the organization.

Education and Public Sector
(a) United States
Uses of IV in education and public service training are much more widespread in the United States than in Europe. Twenty per cent of schools already use laser videodiscs, although it must be said that most of these are simply used with standalone videodisc players as a more durable and more controllable source of video playback. However, large numbers of IV systems have been developed by universities and publishers, helped no doubt by the greater penetration of videodisc technology in the United States and the much lower proportion of domestic and educational use of videotape as compared to the UK and Europe.

The State of Florida Department of Health has a programme to deliver training for approximately 500 new social workers annually using interactive video. They report an average reduction in training time of 25 per cent.

The other revealing finding of this project is that the time now taken by individual trainees to complete the training varies from 60 to 194 hours. This emphasizes the fact that IV allows trainees to work at their own pace, and that this preferred pace of learning does indeed differ widely between individuals.

(b) Europe
Use of IV in the educational sector in Europe has tended to be rare: Europe and in particular the UK make much greater use of video cassette recorders than the United States, and this has tended to prevent the purchase of the standalone videodisc players which were bought in much greater numbers in the United States and Japan.

In both the UK and Europe, uses of IV in the educational sector have either been in the form of research projects in the higher and further education sectors, or in the form of government- supported projects operating in selected schools. Thus the French Ministry of Education has sponsored the installation of IV hardware in a number of schools — although with little or nothing in the way of courseware to run on these systems. In the UK the Open University has produced materials for its summer school students — the Teddy Bear Disc and the Physics of Water, for example.

So far very few schools in the UK have interactive video systems other than Domesday systems, and this is not surprising considering the costs involved. A good many local authorities have taken advantage of the special offers available on

Domesday systems; up to 150 schools are likely to benefit from being involved in the DTI-backed Interactive Video in Schools (IVIS) project; and four schools in the North West of England have received interactive video workstations as part of their involvement in IBM's Personal Computer (PC) in Schools project.

However, manufacturers are aware of the financial problems in public sector education, and educational discounts are available on hardware. In the longer term, interactive video workstations may soon be available to education at a more reasonable cost — no more in real terms, say, than the earliest generation of video cassette recorders over ten years ago.

The Domesday Project employs mixed IV techniques. Mostly it is an amazingly dense pictorial database, using the storage capacity of the videodisc to hold 65 000 maps and photographs, sequences of moving video and many megabytes of computer data which can be searched and viewed in many different ways. It is estimated that one user would need seven years to explore all Domesday's possibilities.

The BBC's Ecodisc puts users in charge of a nature reserve. They must decide on courses of action either on ecological grounds or in response to local pressures. The manager must then cope with the consequences of these decisions.

The IVIS project has developed interactive video programmes to cover a range of curriculum areas including environmental studies, social and personal education, design, geography, science, maths, French and in-service teacher training.

The North West Educational Computing Project (NWECP), one of the PC in Schools projects supported by IBM UK Trust and based at Lancashire Polytechnic, has developed many hours of IV programmes to teach French and German using both off-the-shelf and specially made videodiscs. A detailed case study dealing with this project may be found in Chapters 4 and 5.

The Interactive Science Laboratory, published by John Wiley, makes available scientific experiments which would be too expensive or dangerous to mount in the school or college laboratory.

Industrial Training
(a) United States
Training is by far the largest single use of IV in the United States as it is in Europe. It is impossible to give a complete picture of this sector, but the following gives an overview.

General Electric's Videodisc Interactive Interactive System for Training and Aiding (VISTA) runs 20 videodiscs for in-house staff training and for joint programmes with the Department of Labor on basic machining techniques.

Chrysler have developed IV safety training prescribed by the US Occupational Safety and Health Administration for 85 000 of their production workers. The training involves handling dangerous chemicals and is carried out using portable videodisc self-teaching stations in 31 plants. There is one station per 900 workers and a high degree of efficiency and economy is reported.
(b) Europe
In the UK, nearly one third of all training applications of IV are aimed at sales, managerial or supervisory staff. There seems to be less emphasis on technical areas

of training than in the United States, and generic courseware in particular has tended to target marketing, customer handling and interviewing skills.

At this point it is essential to mention Interactive Information Systems, the leading company in the UK engaged in the production of generic IV courseware for training. Some of their titles give a good view of the area covered by the IV industry: *'Leading Your Team'* , a four disc series aimed at training supervisors and line managers in management techniques; *'Make the Telephone Work for You'* and *'Make the Telephone Sell for You'* aimed at directed telephone skills for managers and sales staff; and *'Writing for Results'* designed to teach the skill of writing effective business letters.

Archiving
(a) United States
The First Vision Photographic Agency has produced a disc containing 50 000 slides intended as an illustration catalogue for advertising agencies and publishers.

The Library of Congress has been involved in a major optical disc and image processing project. It is their response to a specific and pressing need to be able to index and quickly retrieve items from an enormous and growing document bank. The Congressional Research Service is reported as handling close to half a million requests a year for document retrieval.

The technology involved is different from that employed for training applications of the medium: however, the project has some implications in the area of information handling and also for the design of user interfaces which will allow users with non-technical backgrounds to have easy access to complex facilities.
(b) Europe
In the UK one organization, The Image Bank, is making use of videodisc for archival purposes. The material, which has been developed in the United States, is used as an electronic catalogue of photographs by professional photographers. Many photographic libraries have large numbers of photographs available for use, but cataloguing and searching of the image databases are of course major tasks.

The Image Bank system, which makes use of a two-screen configuration, allows cataloguing of photos across 2500 different categories and, much more important, allows clients to browse through the database in minutes rather than hours.

The company intends to use the system to decentralize its operations by providing systems to major clients, who will then be able to browse through available material at their own locations.

As often happens with large database applications, the company has found that the problem of pressing a videodisc containing a very large number of still images is minor compared to the time and effort involved in cataloguing the database. They report the major project costs for the first disc as stemming from the 18 months required to allow several staff to complete this task.

THE HARDWARE

There will be more detailed discussions of IV hardware later in this book, so this introductory section is included to give an initial overview of the topic and should be used as an index to the more detailed hardware information in chapter 2.

Computers

The most commonly used computer for interactive video is the IBM family of personal computers including the IBM PC, PC XT, PC AT, PS/2 or compatible microcomputer. In general terms, these machines are much more widely used throughout the world than any other and there are also many more software packages and peripherals available for them than there are for other computers.

Video Players

The video source in an IV configuration is either a videotape or videodisc player.

Videotape Systems

Videotape systems are now rather old-fashioned and significantly lacking in facilities. However, they are still in use in organizations who decided to invest in IV some time ago and they have some support in situations —especially in education — where cost is an important factor, or where there is a need to change the video material in use repeatedly and often. Within the category of videotape players there is a further distinction between systems using domestic standard machines and tapes such as VHS, and those which use the professional U-Matic standard.

Videodisc Systems

Videodisc formats are divided between Laservision and VHD. VHD discs have now fallen out of favour for interactive use, and all manufacturers have standardized on laservision. Here again, there are different formats which are fully discussed in Chapter 2.

Different videodisc players vary slightly in the range of facilities they offer but their most important feature is that they allow very fast random access to any part of the videodisc.

Screens

IV systems must be capable of displaying both video and computer signals.Some systems solve this problem by using two screens — a television screen for the video picture and a separate monitor for the computer output. Other programmes prefer to use the same screen for both, in which case it is necessary to use a bi-or multi- standard monitor capable of handling both types of information, and some kind of device to allow the mixing of computer and video output on the same screen.

Overlay Boards

Overlay boards are used if graphics or text need to be displayed on top of the video picture, ie on the same screen.

THE MEDIUM

To determine the true nature of IV as a medium it is important to understand the parent technologies of computer-based training (CBT) and video. Many of the techniques of CBT are to be found in IV programmes and it is necessary to understand both their usefulness and their limitations.

Computer Based Training

CBT is one of the many acronyms used to denote the use of computers for teaching or training. The most frequently used abbreviations are:
- CBT — computer based training
- CBI — computer based instruction
- CAI — computer assisted instruction
- CAL — computer assisted (or aided) learning
- TBT — technology based training

The most generally understood benefits of computer-aided learning are individualization, student control, motivation and self-pacing. Computers have been used for training since their early days, notably in the United States. Since it is only relatively recently that personal computers with sufficient processing power to deliver significant training opportunities have been available, much of the early experience in designing materials was acquired in institutions which had access to main- frame computers. Not surprisingly, this tended to mean universities and large commercial organizations in the United States.

Some feel that an unfortunate result of these origins has been that the educational uses of computing were heavily influenced in their infancy by the educational theories of the time. They believe that much of the rather mechanical drill and practice, and much of the reliance on behavioural theory which are still to be found in some instructional software can be traced directly to the fashionable but rigid philosophies of the fifties and sixties.

Types of educational uses of computers include:
- tutorial
- drill and practice
- simulation
- dialogue
- trigger

Tutorial
These programs aim to present information broken down into steps and manageable segments, and lead students through to understanding and mastery by exposition, questioning, feedback and testing.

Drill and Practice
Drill and practice programs do not teach new information or skills, but confine themselves to practising knowledge which has been acquired elsewhere — perhaps through another computer program, or perhaps in some other way.

Simulation
Simulations are based on the concept of a more-or-less authentic model of a situation. Users are presented with a scenario and interact with the program by making decisions, and making their responses to the reactions of the program.

The best known types of computer simulation are adventure games which make use of fantasy. Simulations are especially valuable in subject areas in which discovery, exploration or problem solving are appropriate learning techniques.

Dialogue
Many educational computer programs take on the character of a dialogue at times, but there are a few which attempt to simulate the reactions of an intelligent being in provoking and responding to communications from the user. The best known program of this type is 'Eliza', in which a very cleverly designed program engages in a dialogue with the user and apparently makes a sympathetic 'counsellor's' response to every conversational gambit offered by the user.

Trigger
Some educational programs are unusual in that they are not designed for one-to-one use, but to be exploited by pairs, small groups, or even class-sized groups. The benefit of such programs is often seen as being not so much the interaction between users and system as the interactions between the users themselves, or the general group discussions which are triggered by the programs.

There are times when this form of interaction can be particularly valuable.One example is in language schools, where a group of learners of English are of different nationalities and can only communicate with each other in the target language. In this case, the use of a computer program which promotes discussion is of incalculable value.

Video
There are many benefits from the use of video.

Authenticity
Video can show real behaviour, processes, situations and events. Surroundings can be authentic instead of simulated, real equipment can be used instead of diagrams or verbal descriptions , interactions between people can be shown instead of described.

Access to the inaccessible
On video it is possible to show places which viewers could not normally visit, either because they are too remote, too expensive or too dangerous. It can also provide very clear close-up views for all viewers, where every member of a class or group would not necessarily have a clear view of a particular piece of apparatus.

Trigger Video
The importance of trigger video is increasingly understood. Natural events are shown and then paused at a moment of decision or controversy. This can be far more effective in stimulating discussion and responsive group dynamics than more conventional strategies.

Entertainment
Video and broadcast television represent by far the most popular, widespread and powerful form of mass entertainment. This factor should not be underestimated: the medium is associated in the public mind with the delivery of entertainment, and therefore a large proportion of users are likely to be favourably disposed towards it from the start.

Dramatization
A dramatized situation can be deliberately much less indeterminate than the real thing, so it is possible to highlight and focus on the specific training point. It is possible in a short scene lasting maybe 90 seconds, to put across a very clear and interesting message in a succinct and effective way. It is also possible to indicate the passage of time through video techniques, such as fades, without actually incurring the waste of time which may be suffered when viewing an event in real time.

Enhanced Presentation
Video material is prepared in advance with very great care and skill, and very careful attention can be paid to the selection, layout, presentation and timing of the materials. In addition, it is possible to employ a whole arsenal of effects, including background music, visual effects and graphics, slow motion, fades and so on. Professional presenters or actors can also be employed who can be selected specifically to give exactly the desired impression.

Potential problems with video
(a) Audience expectation
It is important not to disappoint user expectation by providing poor quality material. Today's television programmes represent an incredibly high level of sustained technical and creative skill which we all take for granted. Any video material which is seen by its audience as amateurish, inept, boring or slow is likely to cause users to switch off — literally!
(b) Passive viewing
Watching a television programme, can engage the interest and require involvement, but it is a passive experience. It has long been understood by those with experience

of using video as a training medium that playing a video or showing a film is just not enough, and that a number of strategies are necessary if trainees are to derive real benefits.

Furthermore, research findings now exist which indicate that users of interactive video programmes have some tendency to revert to a passive mode of viewing when using the programmes if the designers have not made explicit provision to promote more active involvement.

IV as Computer Enhanced Video

So what kind of a medium is interactive video? The origins of the medium are at least partly in the corporate video world, and it is not surprising that many of the commercial producers of IV seem to regard it as largely a video medium. They clearly perceive the extra benefits of the medium, but generally view it as video controlled and managed by computer. This view is particularly marked when considering the more old fashioned interactive videotape configurations, where it is really very difficult technically to do much more than present video sequences interspersed with CBT sessions. The limitations of response time caused by the use of videotape reduce the true interactivity of the systems.

However, there are other reasons why some view IV as essentially a video medium. Costs and the present working practices of the industry themselves tend to place a very high — some would say an unjustifiably high — value on the video component. Video production is by far the largest single cost item of most IV projects, and it is difficult to get away from the simplistic equation: highest cost = highest importance.

IV projects often begin with creative (ie video) specialists working with training specialists on an essentially video concept. Software is often seen as an item to be added later in the project, either by an instructional designer working with an authoring language, or by a programmer who is required to implement the designer's specification.

Not surprisingly, those who come to the technology from the world of video see it as an essentially video medium enhanced by the power of the computer.

Thus Wright and Nelson in '*Interactive Media*' state: 'So far much IV has been CBT led. This has had a stifling effect on the input of ideas and the potential of videodisc has not been fully exploited. It has not allowed the V part of IV to come into its own.'

IV as Video Enhanced CBT

Other IV producers see the medium as a type of CBT which is enhanced by the use of video as a resource. Thus there is no conceptual difference between the computer adventure game which uses text and graphics screens to create a microworld around which the user travels, and the game which uses graphics stored as analogue video on a videodisc. The interest for them lies in the interactions, control, random access possibilities and individualization of experience which the computer allows. Those with such views may even recommend the use of video sequences as a cheaper and more economical way of providing high quality graphics than graphics programming. The pictures may be better quality, but the concepts are unchanged.

Not surprisingly, those who enter IV from computing tend to see it as a computer medium enhanced by the power of video. Fuller in *'Interactive Media'* states:'From one point of view interactive video is computer-based education illustrated with video images.'

The True Nature of the Medium

Educationalists or trainers urge designers to give careful thought to the different roles played by the video and the computer at different stages of an IV programme. They often ask questions during the evaluation of a programme, such as 'what exactly is the video doing in this segment?' or 'what part is the computer playing here?'

We believe that all these approaches are misguided. If an IV programme is very clearly weighted on the side of video or computing or if it allows users or evaluators to differentiate easily between the video and computing components at various points, then it has not achieved the seamless blend of video, computing and design of which the medium is capable. IV has the potential to be neither video nor computing but a completely new medium for which we are only just beginning to determine appropriate uses and methodologies. However, it is vitally important to stress that the software component of an IV programme is often undervalued, is critical in its importance and is the element which permits or denies full realization of the aims of the content and instructional designers. It seems strange to us that organizations producing or commissioning IV seem willing to spend so much of their project budget on video and so little on software.

Finally we should add here that we know of no IV projects which have failed or run into serious difficulties because of problems with video production; on the other hand we know of several projects which have met partial or total failure or serious delays because of problems with software or instructional design.

THE VIDEO RESOURCES

We will now look practically at the video resources it is necessary to assemble in order to put together an IV package.

Tape

We will assume that no reputable organization would contemplate the use of off-air recordings in breach of copyright. In-house shooting using some domestic format such as VHS is often suggested as a low-cost option. The savings in cost which this approach makes possible are almost the only conceivable advantage of adopting this standard, but for a fuller discussion see Chapters 2 and 3.

The use of the professional U-Matic format is a possibility if your organization has access to in-house shooting and editing facilities, if your courseware does not need to be very sophisticated and if the video material you wish to use is obtainable within the organization — and especially if it is likely to change rapidly.

However, most of the commercial costs of video lie in the production of the video master tape. If you have to hire in video shooting and editing then you might as well press a videodisc for an extra 10 per cent of your video budget — the additional facilities it will offer are well worth the extra cost.

Disc

If you have decided on a disc-based system you will need to decide whether you can make use of an existing, commercially available videodisc, or if you need to produce one specifically for your needs.

Off-the-shelf discs

See Chapter 2 on videodisc formats for necessary information about active-play (CAV) videodiscs, which are the only laservision discs which can be used interactively. You will find lists of commercially available discs from the BBC and the Pioneer and Philips catalogues. However, if you should find usable material from these sources, discs marketed by BBC Home Video, for example, cannot be used outside the home without breach of the conditions of sale.

Another possible source of usable videodisc material is organizations which have commissioned or produced discs for their own use in IV systems and may be willing to supply the discs independently to third parties. Such discs are likely to be very expensive compared to entertainment titles.

Dedicated videodiscs

If you decide to produce a videodisc specially for your project, it is necessary to determine what kind of footage is required and whether location shooting will be needed. Shooting can be done using 16mm film, 1"C (broadcast quality video), hi-band U-Matic or Betacam. Some companies will even accept VHS footage for pressing to videodisc, but in general it is unwise to go below professional or semi-professional quality. Remember — using any kind of existing footage other than film or video wholly owned by the commissioning organization may involve enormously long-drawn out difficulties over copyright and is not recommended unless there are very pressing reasons or advantages.

The shooting of dedicated video is a high-cost option often quoted at between £1000 and £2000 per minute of finished video. However, it can prove cheaper in the long run than a search for usable existing materials, and one could do worse than to consider the possibility of defraying the cost by selling surplus discs to other projects when they are available. See also Chapter 3 for an outline of ways to obtain high quality video rather more economically.

Quite apart from the practical considerations of obtaining material, video material shot with a particular project in mind will always be infinitely superior to any off-the-shelf disc or tape for the specific purposes of that project. The balance between cost, availability and suitability is crucial in the planning of any IV project.

IMPLEMENTATION

Project Planning

Let us look first at a fairly standard outline of the stages of IV production. This is very much the sort of approach which will be adopted if you commission an IV production house to produce your programme. With this kind of approach, you will receive solid and dependable 'standard' IV courseware.

The following lists the stages of the plan. It is the project manager's task to supervize the proper implementation of all these elements. More detailed discussion will follow in Chapters 4 and 5.

Stage One
- Identify training requirements
- Specify Aims
- Define objectives
- Assess resources
- Decide IV delivery system configuration

Stage Two
- Produce design outline
- Produce storyboard or script
- Produce design document with branching and learning sequence

Stage Three
- Agree design outline, storyboard and script
- Obtain existing video and artwork
-• Brief production specialists

Stage Four
- Shoot video
- Produce or commission stills and artwork
- Produce software programs
- Design and produce packaging, disc labels, disc sleeves

Stage Five
- Edit video material
- Field correlate video material
- Produce master tape
- Check software functionality with video cassette or check disc

Stage Six
- Produce videodiscs
- Integrate discs and software
- Carry out final quality control and testing

Deciding on a configuration

Decisions about what precise hardware configuration to adopt will depend on a number of factors, including some or all of the following:

(a) The situation in which the workstation will be used. For example, will it be made available without supervision in an area generally accessible to staff, or in a training area with support personnel on hand?

(b) The existing skills of users. Are they familiar with keyboards, or will it improve the confidence of non computer-literate staff to use a mouse or other pointing device?

(c) What inputs will be required while working the programs.

(d) What will it cost? A touch sensitive screen may appear to be an appropriate input method, for example, but if it costs ten times as much as a mouse then it is going to have to be ten times as effective or reliable to justify itself.

Software

Once the video material has been committed to disc and the physical elements of the system have been assembled the computer software needs to be incorporated.

Programming an IV configuration usually takes one of two routes: authoring or professional programming.

Authoring

Authoring software is essentially used by subject experts to provide a framework for creating educational material using video and textual information.

Authoring is based on simple computer commands for, typically, question and answer sessions, response analysis and testing. The benefit is that the subject expert has control over the developing software. The disadvantages include limited computational facilities and graphics and slower execution. A professional programmer can use the computer facilities to deliver a high performance system in an efficient and effective way.

The problem, of course, is that an authoring language that is genuinely simple to use must also by definition be very limited in the facilities it provides. On the other hand, the more flexible and powerful an authoring language becomes, the more difficult it becomes to use.

(a) Authoring Packages

The term 'authoring package' is often used to mean a very easy-to-use and very limited authoring facility. Often it takes the form of a specific type of exercise, test or question/answer routine provided as a shell for the novice author to enter suitable material. Thus, one might simply be asked to enter the start and end frame numbers of the desired video sequence and then type in five multiple choice questions with their associated correct answers. The authoring package would itself handle all the processing required to produce the standard lesson.

(b) Authoring systems

An authoring system is usually tied to a particular hardware configuration — often it might be referred to as an authoring station. It would be made up of a particular microcomputer, video source, interface and authoring software. Authors then use this workstation to create courseware to be run on delivery systems based on similar components or a subset of them.

Programming

Professional programming involves a computer programmer implementing a program using a computer language such as Pascal, 'C' or Prolog.

Professional programming can deliver a much higher performance from the IV system, but needs to be done by a software professional.

The Project Team

You will see many estimates of the types of people required to make up the interactive video project team. We will explain the different job titles you will come across, but of course one team member may be able to supply more than one area of expertise.

Subject Expert

The subject expert is the person who knows about what is to be taught. For example, in a project for foreign language training the subject expert is the language specialist.

Teaching expert

It is necessary that the project team should involve someone who has substantial experience of teaching the subject to the appropriate target group. It is likely, though not essential, that the subject and teaching experts will be one and the same.

Instructional designer

The instructional designer's expertise lies in the use of CBT techniques, and it is the responsibility of this team member to translate the requirements of the subject and teaching experts into a format suitable for the medium. It is usual in IV for the instructional designer to be responsible for the authoring of courseware where no software specialist is employed.

Video Expert

Expertise is needed in organizing and directing the video shoot, editing the raw footage, overseeing the pre-mastering process and delivering the finished master tape to the disc pressing facility. It is important to note the difference between the programme making expertise of experts trained in a traditional TV or film-making environment and the specialized requirements of video production and editing for IV use.

Software specialist

Software development involves the analysis of the task to be performed, the design of the solution and finally the writing of the programs (or coding) which will perform these tasks. We feel that the importance of proper software development is greatly underestimated in the IV industry.

Hardware technician

If a very specialized configuration is to be adopted using an unconventional input medium or peripheral device, for example, it may be necessary to design or adapt special components. There are a number of examples of this kind of device being added to an IV configuration.

One example is the famous cardiopulmonary resuscitation programme mentioned earlier (see p 4), in which tuition in resuscitation techniques is carried out by the IV programme and the user tries out these techniques on a dummy which is a part of the configuration.

Another very interesting example of this use of special additional hardware is a much more recent programme by the same designer, David Hon, intended to teach welding skills. An actual welding nozzle is connected to the system to provide tuition and an extremely realistic simulation. Users actually finish by 'welding' a 3" butt weld shown on the display screen, using the nozzle which emits light rather than heat. The system monitors exactly the user's performance. Feedback is given either by showing the result of a particular attempt in visuals on screen, or by stopping the simulation to advise the user about such things as angle of presentation.

Graphic artist

Presentation of material is also an important consideration, both on screen and off. The appearance of the packaging and documentation of the materials as well as the screen layout, choice of colours and standard of graphics, can all substantially influence the frame of mind with which users approach training materials. Here in developed western nations we take for granted, and expect as the norm, the very high standards of graphic design and presentation which surround us at all times.

Skills Convergence

Interactive video is the result of a convergence of technologies, techniques and skills including computing and computer assisted learning, education and training, and video. A complex IV project might require contributions from a large project team with very diverse experience and skills. The larger the team, the greater are the difficulties of integration and mutual understanding they are likely to experience.

Some likely problems are as follows:

(a)   In-fighting between the various disciplines stemming from difficulties in communication.

(b)   Lack of understanding of other disciplines.

(c)   Difficulties of co-ordinating the various contributions.

(d)   Unwillingness (or inability) to accept that the new medium requires a flexibility and freshness of approach .

(e)   Unwillingness to make the effectiveness of the finished courseware the prime consideration. With the best motives, individuals may feel that the needs of their own specialism should assume most importance in the overall plan.

Project Management

The tasks of the project manager can range from the management, scheduling, integration, control and supervision of activities, the control of budgets, the preparation of plans and reports, through to diplomatic activities such as the reconciliation of different points of view and priorities, and the soothing of egos.

We believe that, as long as suitably professional skills are available when required, small is beautiful when it comes to the IV project team. It is important to have a good overview of all project activities and to control budgets, time and expertise. This is easier to achieve within the context of a small operational team in close touch with each other.

REASONS FOR CHOOSING IV

It is one thing for academic institutions to embark on research projects, the purpose of which may be to establish the potential of IV for particular purposes; it is quite another for a commercial organization to commit itself to the development of courseware which will cost tens of thousands of pounds to implement. It is, therefore, important to consider very carefully your reasons for adopting IV as a response to training needs.

There are many reasons for wishing to adopt IV. They may be any of the following:

(a)   You have a training need or problem which only the facilities of IV can solve.

(b)   You wish to reduce training costs by reducing staffing.

(c)   You wish to reduce training costs by delivering training at the work place instead of removing trainees from it.

(d)   You wish to improve the efficiency of training.

(e)   You wish to compensate for the shortage of skilled staff or subject expertise.

(f)   It is too dangerous to lay on a real training simulation to teach the target skill.

(g)   It is too expensive to lay on a real training simulation to teach the target skill.

(h)   You wish to provide a quality or type of training which is unobtainable in any other way.

(i)   You are technology led — you have heard of interactive video, you are aware it is a fashionable high-tech medium and wish to explore ways of exploiting it.

Chapter 2

HARDWARE

INTRODUCTION

To anyone not familiar with the technology, the term 'interactive video' or 'IV' might not be particularly enlightening. A better understanding may be gained by a definition such as 'computer-controlled video' or 'computer-driven video' or even 'the combination of computer processing and video images'. However, even these definitions can't properly portray the power, flexibility and effectiveness that an IV system can bring to most training situations.

Just over a decade ago the seeds of the modern IV system were sown by simultaneous developments in the computing and video industries. At the end of the 1970s a revolutionary development took place in the computing industry with the introduction of the personal computer. The personal computer (PC) had at its heart a microprocessor the size of a thumb nail; the computing power it provided previously occupied a large air-conditioned room!

At around the same time, the development of the videotape and videodisc were taking place in the video industry. It was coincidental, but fortuitous, that videodiscs and the PC came onto the scene around the same time, allowing the two technologies to develop side by side and ultimately converge into the new and exciting technology of interactive video.

Functionality of the IV system

The hybrid nature of this new medium exploits the properties of the videodisc and combines its benefits with the processing power of the PC, providing the trainer or educationalist with the most advanced technological tool for the delivery of educational material.

Typically a standard IV configuration will consist of a microcomputer, videodisc player, monitor, input medium such as a keyboard or a mouse, a hardware interface between the computer and the videodisc player, and the videodiscs themselves.

Such a system typically functions in the following way:
-   the computer software controls the interaction and functions of the videodisc player;
-   the videodisc player emits one video signal and two audio signals under the supervision of the computer;
-   the three signals are transmitted from the player to the computer before being output to the monitor and loudspeaker;
-   the computer software controls the generation of the text and graphics and the display of video images onto the monitor;

- the software determines the display of computer-generated material, video material or a combination of both;
- the decision as to what is displayed on the monitor will usually be taken in response to the users' input;
- the user interacts with the system via a keyboard, mouse, touch screen or any other input device.

A most important factor is that the user is involved with the system from the outset and has the ability to control the system available simply and effectively.

One distinction to draw immediately is the difference between interactive video and linear video. Like television, conventional linear video is a passive medium. The user may react to the programme on the screen but has very little or no control over it. By contrast, IV affords the user complete control over the pace and delivery of the programme content.

Compatibility within the system

The physical elements of an IV system are subject to the various standards that abound in the computing and video industries. But since the video material, and possibly digital data, is stored on a videodisc and optically read by a laser beam, there is also the problem of standards for optical storage!

This latter problem has perhaps been the least of the IV developer's worries, but there is no doubt that the multiplicity of computing and video standards has had a braking effect on the development of IV. Compatibility can still be a source of confusion for any would-be practitioner.

The good news is that the standard microcomputer, the IBM PC and its compatibles, and the laservision standard set by Phillips, now seem to have become accepted as the de facto component standards for IV systems.

Having arrived at these two standards, the problem of connectivity is then raised. The digital output from the computer and the analogue source from the videodisc player will have to be generated on to one screen or some other output medium.

For this, a hardware interface is necessary which can combine the signals from the computer and the videodisc and send it to the output display. This interface is housed inside the computer on one, or possibly two, expansion slots. Since its launch in September 1985, the Videologic MIC—2000 interface series — the first interface system on the UK market — and its subsequent variations have dominated the IV scene. The result has been the acceptance of the MIC system as the standard 'common-ground' between the computer and the videodisc player. It is estimated that 95 per cent of IV applications in Europe based on the IBM/Philips laservision standard, use the MIC hardware interface.

This standardization has clarified peoples' perceptions of what IV is and what it's capable of, and has led to a surge in IV applications. Another benefit of standardization has been the proliferation of hardware accessories for IV systems, based on the de facto standards, which now makes it possible to 'mix and match' the hardware elements of a system to best fit a particular need. There is also no need to worry about compatibility should you develop new or apply existing ready-made IV programmes.

Successful implementation of IV depends far more on the application of the technology and the environment in which it is applied, rather than the technology itself.

TYPES OF VIDEODISC SYSTEM

The concept of the videodisc — a disc of audio LP-like proportions containing both video and audio — is not new and since the first patent for a videodisc is credited to John Logie Baird as far back as October 1926, it can't even be said to be recent.

Mechanical

The mechanical system employed methods comparable to normal audio recording, where a continuous, modulated groove is cut into the disc. A stylus then tracks the modulated spiral and the resulting movements are converted into picture signals. There are now no videodisc systems based on mechanical playback.

Electromagnetic

This method for recording material on a videodisc uses equivalent techniques to those used in videotape recording. Video signals are converted to electronic signals with the actual recording making magnetic patterns on metallized plastic. For playback the process is essentially reversed where the magnetic patterns are converted back into video signals.

Systems based on this recording method are extremely expensive and no available IV system uses electromagnetic technology.

Capacitance

This is the technology which is used by the very high density(VHD) system offered by JVC and Thorn-EMI.

The system relies on information being encoded onto the grooveless videodisc as capacitance variations, which depend on a spiral pattern of variable length depressions in the PVC surface of the disc. These variations are then detected by a stylus on travelling over the surface.

Running parallel to the video and audio tracks is a control track which keeps the stylus in the correct position, allowing the stylus to be positioned anywhere on the disc. VHD discs are primarily intended for linear footage. In order to access a still frame, one picture is required on each revolution which means that the picture has to be recorded twice on the disc. This effectively reduces the number of still frames per side by half to around 25 000, and also means that still frames have to be decided in advance.

A VHD disc is fragile and susceptible to damage from dust particles or scratches so it is housed in a protective caddy which is automatically loaded and unloaded by the player.

The VHD disc has not made significant inroads into the IV market probably because of its drawbacks in terms of video footage and robustness. The main company marketing the system in the UK, Thorn- EMI has now adopted optical recording techniques for videodisc systems.

Optical

Optical technology is the most complex of videodisc systems, but offers the best quality pictures and is ideal for IV applications.

This is the technology of the laservision system developed by Philips, also used by Sony and Pioneer. For IV applications the laservision system is the standard on which almost all training and educational programmes are developed.

The system is detailed later in this chapter but basically the video, audio and control information is encoded on the videodisc using a high-powered laser, and the information is then coated by a thin layer of aluminium, which gives the videodisc its distinctive mirror-like finish. This information is then sealed within a perspex-like surface which makes the disc robust and able to tolerate scratches and fingerprints.

Playback is obtained by a low-powered laser, from the videodisc player, scanning the surface of the disc to obtain the information which decodes into pictures, audio and the necessary digital information.

A laservision videodisc holds one frame per revolution as against two frames by the VHD system. This means that any frame, whether as part of moving footage or a still, can be frozen at will. The capacity of the disc is 54 000 frames which is equivalent to 36 minutes moving footage and also either two audio tracks or 320 megabytes of digital information per side.

NEBRASKA SCALES

In 1979 the Nebraska Videodisc Production Group in the USA popularized the concept of 'levels of interactivity' as a scale devised to identify the potential for interactivity of the various IV systems.

When a system is described in terms of the Nebraska Scale, the description is aimed at the capabilities of the component hardware, the videodisc player and its controlling device.

This scaling doesn't apply to the interactive involvement of the end user, nor is it meant as a measure of courseware production. It is purely a reference for IV hardware.The Scale, although perhaps of less importance due to the quality of hardware and availability of IV specific enhancements, is still useful for an appreciation of where the technology began, how it has developed and also as terms of reference for interactive hardware of all kinds.

There are five levels of interactivity defined, numbered zero through to four.

Level Zero

Level zero essentially identifies the use of interactive videodiscs in linear mode of play without interruption. Usage is generally restricted to entertainment or perhaps training presentations to be viewed from beginning to end.

Level One

At this level the videodisc players are domestic in nature and have the attributes of control normally associated with the common videotape recorder. At this level the player can either be controlled by a panel of buttons on the front of the player or, more commonly, by a remote hand-held controller. The following basic features are present in level one videodisc players:
-    play forward/reverse
-    scan forward/reverse - remote control
-    still frame
-    random access
-    frame search
-    slow motion forward/reverse
-    step frame
-    two audio tracks

There is no real interactivity at this level. The player is simply a facility for very fast retrieval of video pictures with the added bonus of perfect quality still pictures accurate to 1/25 of a second.

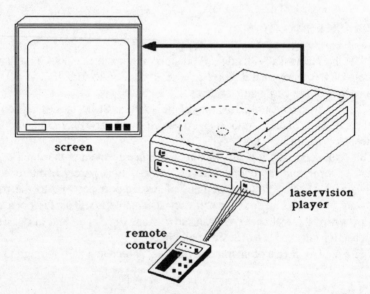

Figure 1 Level 1 Configuration

This level really identifies the domestic use of the early videodisc and no serious training applications have developed at this level.

However a system at this level is extremely cheap to buy — all you need is a domestic, or industrial, videodisc player and a television monitor — and you can then browse through available videodiscs and begin to appreciate just what is possible with higher level systems.

Many of the early IV practitioners still use a level one system for cataloguing the frame numbers on the videodisc.

Level two

At this level come industrial model videodisc players. Players at this level have all the features of level one players plus an erasable programmable read only memory (EPROM) slot.

An EPROM can be programmed to guide a user through specified video sections or stills. An IV system with level two facilities comprises the industrial videodisc player, a screen display and a keypad. This is the level where interactivity begins to take place.

The computer program to run the application is stored on the EPROM which is plugged into the videodisc player. The computer program on the EPROM is then loaded into the central processing unit (CPU) onboard the player.

The computer program is then executed which gives more power to the system as elementary computer control is incorporated with the video pictures.

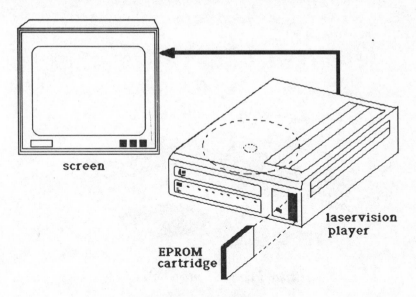

Figure 2 Level 2 Configuration

Typical additions to the system features at this level are branching facilities and decision making powers enacted by learner input from the keypad. This allows for tangential paths to be taken for special needs or complexity.

The drawbacks at this level are the costs of developing an EPROM cartridge against the relatively low level of computing power available through the player's onboard microprocessor. The graphics overlay is limited to teletext which is cumbersome and slow in comparison to the fast picture access times of the laser.

An EPROM cartridge also has a memory capacity of only 48k, due to the onboard

CPU, which in computer data terms renders it redundant for any serious training applications. It could be extremely beneficial in situations where a service is provided such as journey directions, point of sale or information applications and elementary training courses.

However, the greater flexibility and control compared to level one systems can prove to be very valuable.

Level Three

Level three systems are the most widely used in IV. At this level a microcomputer is attached to the videodisc player and provides overall control of the system.

The link is established via a standard RS232 serial communications port in both the computer and the videodisc player. A cable conveys instructions from the computer to the player, with the player responding in a similar fashion with acknowledgements of the acceptance or completion of the computers' command. Effectively the player is controlled in the same slave fashion as any other peripheral device.

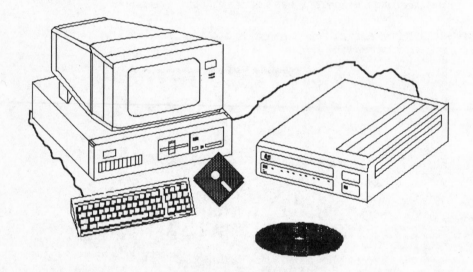

Figure 3 Level 3 Configuration

This type of system is limited in flexibility, apart from obvious hardware restrictions, only by the software which drives it. Indeed a single videodisc resource can be utilized in a variety of ways by the computer, either to alter the presentation of the material or vary the level of complexity. The result could be an extended life- span of developed courseware since the computer material is volatile and easily updated. Two audio tracks are available, along with the video signal, which can be used for different commentaries. Possibly two languages can be used, or the commentaries can be of differing complexity, or the channel which carries the two audio tracks can be used to convey digital data. You cannot have one track of audio and the other carrying digital data because digital data uses the whole channel.

The very latest in sophisticated text and graphics can be superimposed on the video picture(s) or displayed independently thus providing an extremely powerful audiovisual medium.

This is the level at which the manufactures of videodisc players are mainly pitching their equipment. Level three players have very little onboard intelligence. Instead the emphasis is on the quality of the optical readout assembly within the player, while the 'intelligence' is supplied by the computer.

A level three system portrays the truly versatile nature and flexibility of IV to adapt to almost any training application.

Level Four

The recently defined level four is an IV system which allows the videodisc player to operate as an optical storage drive for the computer as well as its traditional role in an IV configuration.

Digital data stored on the videodisc has to be held in analogue form and is stored on the video and audio frame space. This reduces the amount of video programme time on the videodisc, but the benefit lies in the density of storage for digital data. For example, 100 megabytes of digital data can be stored on what would normally be less than five minutes of moving footage on the videodisc.

In digital storage terms the videodisc is the densest storage medium currently available. Level four systems incorporate significant advances in the technology.

Perhaps some future system will effectively take us back to the original concept of domestic IV systems with the introduction of compact disc interactive or digital-video interactive which will develop IV as a truly mass market with many applications at a price everyone can afford.

VIDEO STANDARDS

The linking together of computers with video is not a new idea but it is a subject which can cause much misunderstanding with many a costly mistake to be made. The last five years or so has seen a bewildering growth of audiovisual media in all areas of business and industry.

More and more people and companies are developing audiovisual presentations from inception to implementation which includes preparation, shooting and editing. Whereas previously when one could afford to be blissfully ignorant of even the technical basics, and all that was required to show a video was to understand the meaning of a couple of buttons on a video player, any attempt at video production must be apj roached in serious manner.

Good qu lity video production is a professional field and amateur producers will almost certainly get their fingers burned. Probably more confusion exists about standards for IV than any other aspect of video.

A major part of any IV system is the production of a video picture, stored on the videodisc, projected onto a display monitor. Television and video pictures we take for granted, not needing to know the technicalities of how the images are reproduced on our screen. Television programmes shot for American TV differ in the way they are recorded from those shot for UK television. This is irrelevant to the viewer watching the programme since before the pictures reach a UK TV set they are converted from the American standard to the format which enables transmission throughout Britain. The same applies to the home video market where all releases conform to the video standards which can be shown on a British domestic television set.

The difference with a videodisc is that once you have recorded the material in a certain format you cannot change it. This means that video footage shot in the UK and pressed to videodisc by a disc manufacturer such as Philips, needs a type of videodisc player which is capable of playing that type of disc. The problem arises that if a disc is pressed in America then it too will need an adapted videodisc player to reproduce the video pictures. The two are, not surprisingly, incompatible and this is the first distinction to make between IV systems. For in-house productions this may mean pressing videodiscs in the two formats if the system is intended for the US as well as the UK and European markets. Although there are differences between the European countries they are not insurmountable and any videodisc prepared to UK standards should perform on the continent. A company wishing to buy off-the-shelf material for use in the UK should make sure that their systems conform to the UK video and television standard.

In order to gain a clear perception of how a video image is created from a videodisc it is necessary to look briefly at the development of colour television technology.

Colour standard

Initially the relationship between television technology and the technology of IV might not seem clear, however the evolution of television technology leads to the first major issue of compatibility for IV.

Because of the broadcast quality of the pictures held on the videodisc, the IV package developed will depend on the respective countries' colour television standard.

Just to add to the problem, there is not one colour television standard in the world but three and each different system is incompatible with the others. The three systems are identified by the initials of their respective colour standards:

- NTSC (American National Television Standards Committee) USA, Canada, Mexico, Japan, South Korea, South America (except Brazil) and the Caribbean;
- PAL (Phase Alternation Line) UK, West Germany, most of Western Europe, Africa, Middle East and Asia;
- SECAM (Séquentiel Couleur à Mémoire) France, USSR, most of the Eastern Bloc, Greece and African countries which have French influence.

This problem of incompatibility does not solely arise from the different colour standards: the problem was caused much earlier by the method each system employs to create a video image on the screen.

The main components in creating this image are the line standard and the field standard. The colour standards which were added in the 1960s served to compound the existing problem.

A video signal, as with any other electrical signal, transports only one piece of information at one time. This means that the detail which composes an image such as the luminance, colour, etc, has to be divided into a large number of discrete points and transmitted one at a time. In television this is done by scanning the image point by point along a line left to right, and repeated line by line from the top of the image to the bottom of the image. In the receiving display monitor or TV set, a corresponding scanning process has to occur to build up the picture. This is the simplest view of generating an image on the screen. It is this scanning process which is responsible for the three differing colour standards of NTSC, PAL and SECAM and therefore, ultimately, for the the development of different videodisc systems.

There are two ways in which the scanning process differs: first the number of lines into which the picture is divided; and second the rate at which the scanning process is repeated, ie the number of frames per second.

Line standard

In the UK, TV broadcasting (apart from the early Baird system) started with a 405—line picture, but this standard was completely replaced by the end of 1984 by the 625—line standard which is used for all colour broadcasting. The number of lines used to make up one screen which describes the line standard.

In the USA, television was introduced with a 525—line picture and that standard still persists today in the Americas, Japan and some other countries. France initially adopted an 819—line standard but have now moved to the 625—line standard. High definition television, which is now becoming a reality, uses up to 1250 lines per picture. The more scanning lines per picture the finer the detail but for the foreseeable future 525—line (NTSC) and the 625—line (PAL and SECAM) systems will continue to dominate.

Field standard

The second major difference between the television standards is the picture rate commonly known as the field standard or frame rate.

Most European nations use 220/240 volts at a frequency of 50 Hertz. Early television technology adopted a frame rate of 50 fields per second to avoid rolling-black bands and portray smooth motion.

Each picture is transmitted as two separate fields. In the first field only the odd lines are transmitted (1,3,5..625), then the second field follows, transmitting lines 2,4,6..624 which are 'interlaced' with the first set of lines. So there are 50 fields per second making up 25 complete pictures.

After the first field is transmitted the electronic beam which 'shoots' the information onto the screen is situated at line 625 and the screen is momentarily blanked while the beam resets itself to line two and begins transmitting the second field. This momentarily blanking of the screen is known as vertical blanking.

All this happens within a fraction of a second and cannot be detected by the naked eye. For the videodisc, which holds one complete picture on each revolution, this means that each track contains two fields composing the actual picture and two areas of vertical blanking.

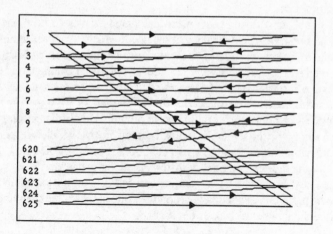

Figure 4 Interlaced Picture Pattern

In the USA the mains frequency is 60Hz so that was the field rate adopted there — 60 fields per second composing 30 pictures or frames per second. Despite advances in the technology, the 50Hz/60Hz distinction still persists. However with the proliferation of different channels, cable TV, satellite broadcasting and the vision of high definition television, perhaps we can look forward to a worldwide TV standard.

Evolution of colour television technology

The evolution of television technology began long before John Logie Baird's work on mechanical television. Baird was not the only one involved with television in 1923; at least two other pioneers, one in America the other in West Germany, were seriously investigating mechanical television, both of whom had significant engineering resources at their disposal.

Baird had little money or other support and relied on ingenuity and hard work for development. On 15 October 1926 a patent was filed for the first videodisc for a system called Phonovision (in fact Baird went on to patent a simple videodisc player in 1928 but none were ever commercially developed).

The first public demonstration of a complete system scanning 30 lines with a picture repetition rate of 12 per second, was given in January 1926 where the public saw real television with moving objects. Three years later regular broadcasts began and the BBC set up its own television studio in Broadcasting House, using apparatus supplied by Baird.

Throughout the thirties Baird successively improved on the 30 — line standard, first to 60 lines and then 90, 120, and 180 lines. In 1936 the final standard of 240 lines and 25 pictures per second was installed in Alexandra Palace for service trials. By now electronic television had been developed and was also installed in Alexandra Palace for service trials in competition with Bairds' system. Development of electronic television was undertaken principally by EMI in the UK and RCA in the USA. Since both companies were extremely close — RCA had a significant shareholding in EMI — there was some degree of co-operation. In 1935 EMI put forward a 405 — line/50 fields per second interlaced proposal. This was the standard that operated in the service trials, alternating weekly with the 240 — line system of Baird's from 1936 until 1937 when Baird's' mechanical system was dropped.

After World War II the British television service reopened with the original 405 — line standard which lasted for almost another 40 years before being finally closed in January 1985. However by the early sixties an increasing number of European countries had opted for a 625 — line standard and the new BBC2 service began in 1964 on 625 lines followed by the duplication on 625 — lines of existing 405 — line BBC and ITV services using electronic conversion equipment.

Modern television technology has long solved the need to correlate frame rate to power frequency so there is no technical reason for not adopting a worldwide standard for HDTV — perhaps a 1250 — line standard — which would also allow IV packages to be developed for a truly international market.

THE LASERVISION SYSTEM

Laservision is the universal term used to describe the optical videodisc playback system which reproduces high quality television footage with stereo or two-channel sound. Originally adopted by Philips, the company who developed the standard, laservision systems are now made under licence by other major IV manufacturers including Sony and Pioneer, thus providing a much needed standard in the optical disc market.

The audiovisual information for the system (and computer data if required) is carried on a prerecorded videodisc, and a revolutionary optical playback technique is used to read the densely packed information sealed inside the videodisc. As the coded material is optically read by a laser beam penetrating the outer shell of the disc, there is no mechanical contact between the disc and the pick-up so neither the laser nor the disc suffers any wear at all.

Effective communications is the key to any successful training package, and in laservision, a most effective audiovisual communications medium is available.

Although the principles of the laservision system are in part familiar, much of the technology is brand new, producing a system which uses the the very latest in optical technology.

As the term 'laservision' implies, the heart of this optical system is the laser. Invented in the late 1950s, the laser (an acronym for light amplification by stimulated emission of radiation) focuses on the aluminium coated microscopic pits sealed inside the videodisc, and the variations in strength of the reflected beam are detected and demodulated into video and audio signals.

The laservision system comes in two formats: PAL or NTSC. Differences between the systems are detailed in the video standards section (see pp 32-41), but basically the difference in laservision formats is the same as that for colour television.

In order to grasp a greater understanding of the optical disc system it is useful to become more acquainted with its two main components: the videodisc and the videodisc (or laservision) player.

The videodisc

The standard size for laservision discs is 30cm in diameter, which is the same as that of an audio LP and two and a half times that of the standard CD-audio disc. Although similar in appearance to its smaller and 'younger cousin' the CD-audio, the only similarity between a videodisc and an audio LP is that they are both double sided.

Figure 5 A Videodisc

As with all optical storage discs the most striking difference is the mirror-like finish, created by a thin aluminium layer which not only enhances appearance but is also necessary for the reflective operation of the laser beam. However, the real difference between the videodisc, the audio LP and any other analogue storage disc lies in the structure of the recorded information. Rather than a continuously modulated groove the videodisc has a single track of microscopic pits in a highly reflective surface, which carries all the necessary information for colour, broadcast quality, pictures with stereo or two-channel sound and control data for the laservision player.

The recording on the disc contains a series of tiny pits on the reflective surface so that when the laser beam falls on this surface, the effect of the pits and flats is to interrupt the beam reflection. In simple terms the strength of the beam reflection is lessened should the beam fall into a pit. This pattern of interruption is received by the photodiode inside the laservision player and the complete audiovisual signal is assembled from this information.

One side of a videodisc contains around 14 billion of these pits, arranged in a spiral track. The pits are approximately 0.4um wide and 0.1um deep, with the length varying between 0.1 and 0.5um depending on the encoding.

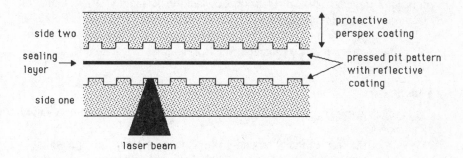

Figure 6 Slice through videodisc showing pits

The track containing the picture, audio and control information is 60 times denser than that of an that of an audio LP and is over 19 miles in length! With such a large amount of information compressed into such a small area the videodisc represents, at present, the densest storage medium in existence.

A recorded track of this density would be irreparably damaged by the tiniest particle of dust or even a fingerprint. However, unlike conventional video footage, the recording is totally protected because it is sealed 'inside' the disc. The recording is totally protected by a perspex-like surface which, at a thickness of 1.25 mm, makes fingerprints, scratches and particles of up to 75 microns in diameter completely tolerable.

The videodisc is produced in two formats to appeal to both IV users and the domestic and entertainment market. The differing formats allow for optimum performance for the different uses. Video footage is held in a different way for IV use because of the need to display still frames and access particular frames very quickly, whereas for feature films there is not the same need for fast direct access to ½ second of the film, nor is there much need for a still frame capacity. The two disc formats are:

- CLV (Constant Linear Velocity)
- CAV (Constant Angular Velocity)

CLV discs

These discs are often referred to as long-play discs principally because they can store more linear footage per side than a CAV disc. However, the trade-off is a loss of flexibility in control and access.

The minimum possible track length is used for each picture frame resulting in the longest playing time — 60 minutes per side — for a 30cm videodisc. Since the track length per revolution increases from one at the inside of the disc to three at the outer edge of the disc, the playback speed varies and slows down towards the edge of the disc as the programme is read. For video footage which is shot to PAL television standards, this means that the speed ranges from 1500rpm to 500rpm.

Generally long-play discs are used for entertainment rather than interactivity since they only have limited control and identification facilities, typically various modes of play including slow motion, fast forward and reverse, but not still frame. Access is generally by elapsed time and is therefore not frame accurate. The bonus of this is an extra 25 minutes or so of linear footage per side.

CAV discs

Generally referred to as active-play discs, these are the type of discs commonly used for IV purposes.

Each side of the disc contains around 36 minutes of moving footage which is composed of some 54 000 picture frames with the information for one picture frame spread out over one track revolution. Unlike CLV discs, active-play discs spin at a constant 1500rpm but, more importantly, they allow the use of all the available control functions on a laservision player. A typical IV programme will make much use of these features, such as the ability to freeze frame, slow motion, step forward and reverse, and many more facilities which we will explore later in this chapter.

All the 54 000 frames on each side of the disc are individually addressable, with each picture having its own number in a normal count sequence beginning with number 1. Each picture frame is held on one track, and because one track is equivalent to one revolution, tracks vary in length and in quality. A track at the outer edge of the disc has much more space to hold the frame information than one which is at the centre of the disc. The innermost tracks are compressed and the outermost tracks elongated. Where compression is greatest the advice from Philips, who make the finished product, is not to have sequences where still frame or slow motion is used. The outermost tracks (bigger pits) are not fully reliable either, because of tracking problems in the moulding process.

In our experience IV programmes which have used still frames outside the advisable optimum range of 10 000 — 45 000 have suffered no observable degradation in quality whatsoever. With each frame individually addressable from the computer with pin-point accuracy, a perfectly still, judder-free picture can be displayed for as long as desired.

Previous sections of this book have explained the differing standards of video embodied in the PAL and NTSC formats. These same variations can again be seen in the different technical specifications of CAV discs conforming to the NTSC format (largely American and Japanese) as against those following the European PAL format.

Technical specifications — CAV discs

	NTSC	PAL
disc diameter	30cm (12")	30cm (12")
line resolution	525 lines	625 lines
disc thickness	2.5mm	2.7mm
playback current	110v/60Hz	220v/50Hz
spin direction	anticlockwise	anticlockwise
rotational speed	1800rpm	1500rpm
playback rate	30 frames/sec	25 frames/sec

In the videodisc a single track of pits, and also flats, carry all the information necessary for full quality, broadcast pictures and stereo, or two-channel sound. In addition to this there is extensive control information which is used by the player to, for example, identify the disc, CAV or CLV, and allow the player to perform the supplementary control facilities depending on the disc type.

The method of coding the information from the master videotape on to the disc is different for each type of disc, with each designed to provide optimal audiovisual signal during playback.

The long-play disc format is aimed principally at the entertainment market and, therefore, the amount of footage on the disc is more important than the ability to access individual frames with absolute accuracy. This allows for 60 minutes of programming on either side.

An active-play disc, on the other hand, is aimed at the IV market where the transfer of knowledge and information is required. Material stored on a CAV disc is therefore organized to allow access operations to be carried out on the recorded programme with a guaranteed accuracy of $\frac{1}{25}$ second. This allows for up to 36 minutes playing time per side.

The information is coded onto the disc with a high-powered laser using a system of direct modulation. It is not necessary to go into the technical detail of the actual coding except to understand that the video frequency modulation and the audio pulse produces a 'clipped' waveform, which in turn is used to produce the pits on the disc. The length and the spacing of the pits, which vary in dimensions, form an analogue code for the video and audio signal.

The method of storing the picture and control information on each disc is:

CAV — each picture, with two fields and two vertical blanking fields occupy one track revolution;

CLV — each frame occupies the same track length with one revolution at the inside, increasing to three frames per revolution at the outside.

How the discs are made

The process of filming and editing a final assembly of the video and audio material known as the 'master-edit' is expounded in the video section of this book. This final master-tape, properly edited to required standards, then goes through a stage called pre-mastering in order to prepare the material for the transfer onto videodisc.

In principle, the discs are made following the same process as audio LP records, but because the finished product is technically much more advanced, the actual production process differs quite considerably. Sterile conditions are required at several stages of the production process.

The first stage of production is mastering; sending the pictures from the pre-mastered videotape through a machine called the laser beam recorder. This consists of a glass plate which has a photosensitive coating on one side. The action of switching the high-powered laser on and off forms the exposures which, after a photographic development process, produces the pattern of microscopic pits along the spiral track.

Having developed the photo-resist layer, the master is then silvered for conductivity and also to protect it before being tested and taken off to be used in the production of the stamper. The glass master is then taken to the plating bath in which it is coated with a thin nickel layer. The production of stampers begins with the metal plate after about three hours in the plating bath, being separated from the glass master to form what is termed the metal 'father'. This father, the first impression, is still too fragile to replicate in any quantity, so by using a galvanic process a 'mother' is produced which is in turn used to produce one or more 'sons'. The sons of this family tree are then used as the stampers for the replication of the actual discs.

It is technically possible to produce tens of thousands of discs from the 300 micron thick stamper. The process of pressing the replicas is done by a technique known as injection moulding which has no detectable wear on the stamper, and works by forcing a plastic mix into a mould at high pressure (200 tons) and a high temperature (275 deg C).

After each replica is pressed an extremely thin layer of aluminium, no more than 0.04um thick, is sprayed over the encoded information providing the essential reflective appearance, which is finally sealed with a protective layer of perspex. As all discs are double sided, the two recordings, produced separately, are then bonded together to produce a double sided disc.

The videodisc player

The videodisc player is an optical playback system which reproduces broadcast quality pictures together with stereo or two-channel audio. The recording is optically read by a low-powered laser beam housed within the player.

The laser beam is guided by high-precision optical components and finally by the objective lens into a spot of 0.9um diameter on the videodisc. Although the internal workings of various players may differ they will essentially consist of three component parts: the disc or turntable drive, the optical system and electronic circuits.

The turntable speed is determined by the control information held on the videodisc which serves to identify the disc type, the present location on the disc and thus spins at the desired rpm for an active or long-playing disc.

The optical system contains the parts necessary to 'read' the information from the videodisc. The optical readout technique involves the laser beam moving radially from the lead-in tracks at the inner radius to the lead-out tracks at the outer radius. In order to achieve this fast and accurate movement of the laser beam, the necessary components are carried on a motor-sledge which moves along a radial path beneath the videodisc. The objective lens which focuses the beam on to the videodisc, to a point 60 times finer than that of a gramophone stylus, is located on the sledge and is servocontrolled. Because of the tolerances involved in the manufacture of both the videodisc and the player it is inevitable that there will a very slight up-and-down movement of the videodisc. These undulations are compensated for by the objective lens under servocontrol, moving in and out to keep the laser correctly focused on the videodisc track at all times.

Exact focusing, tracking and synchronization of the laser beam on the video track is maintained by having the entire optical system under servocontrol, which allows the exceptionally high quality of video and sound.

When the laser beam falls on the flat, highly reflective surface it is reflected. However, as explained earlier, the tracks on the videodisc contain a pattern of minuscule pits which interrupt the beam reflection. It is this pattern of interruption, detected by a photodiode which is situated at the end of the beam return path, which make up the video picture and the accompanying audio. The pattern of interruption is determined by the characteristics of the pits. If the beam falls on the flat, mirrored surface the beam is reflected; if the beam falls 'into' the pit then the intensity of the reflection is greatly reduced, and thus the photodiode builds up the audiovisual signals from the intensity of the laser beam reflections.

Videodisc or videotape?

Throughout this book the term IV implicitly means the use of the optical videodisc. However, in principle, an IV configuration could be composed with a videotape system rather than a videodisc system.

The only difference between an interactive videotape system and an interactive videodisc system is the use of a videotape and a videotape player rather than the optical disc and playback system. In principle both systems work in the same way, with the core element being the computer with a display screen and an interface (if graphics are required to be superimposed over the video images).

However, the advantages of the videodisc system lie in the optical readout method allied with the power of a controlling computer. The videodisc provides a storage medium of unique capabilities. and is the densest storage medium in existence.

This protective shield guarantees lasting picture quality and the optical readout technique avoids wear of the material stored on the disc. The videotape, on the other hand, is extremely susceptible to wear and tear since the material encoded on the tape comes into direct contact with the read/write heads of the videotape player.

Having said that, the videotape has two distinct advantages over the videodisc in that material can be erased and rerecorded many times over, while information encoded onto a videodisc can only be repeatedly read. Also, several hours of playing time is possible with a tape-based system, compared to around 70 minutes maximum provided by the videodisc. Obviously there is degradation in quality of recycled videotapes, but nevertheless the videotape method may prove a useful, cheap, alternative to organizations such as educational establishments, where a simpler audiovisual system will suffice. The actual lifetime of a tape is limited and depends on the frequency of use and on the initial quality of the tape. Since the material on the videodisc is completely protected it has effectively an indefinite lifespan, so a tape based system is not necessarily more economical.

THE INTERFACE SYSTEM

So far we have concentrated on the most visible parts of the system, the computer element and the videodisc element. These are essentially separate sources of information which together make up an IV programme.

It is a trivial task to put either the computer source or the video source onto a single screen, but combining the two signals onto the one output device is no simple operation. On the one hand we have the digital data generated by the computer in the form of graphics and text, and on the other the analogue source from the videodisc. Another piece of hardware is needed to allow moving video footage, transmitted from the videodisc player, to be combined with computer generated material on a single screen.

An interface board which fits into one of the expansion slots in the computer (or possibly two depending on which interface kit is used) will take as inputs the video source from the player and digital data from the computer. Its basic function is to combine these inputs into one output which can then be displayed on screen.

The IV industry refers to this as the overlay capability, where graphics appear to be superimposed on moving, or still, video pictures.

Standards in both the computing and video elements have certainly stabilized IV systems in many ways but the standardization of the hardware interface, along with its software support, is in many ways the key to solving hardware incompatibility. Technology in both the computing and video industries is in an ever advancing state and IV customers are faced with the capital investment in equipment which, because of the pace of change, can soon become dated.

The recent proliferation in IV hardware has meant that prospective users can shop around for different components from different manufacturers, developing a hybrid system with maximum performance in any desired situation. Of course with such an array of hardware to choose from, the problem of incompatibility raises its head again. All the variations that abound in the computing industry have to be taken into consideration including input and output devices, graphics standards, software in general, as well as the actual machine.

Conceptually sited between the hardware elements of the system and offering a standard method of communicating with these various hardware components, through the software, the interface kit guarantees a hardware independent platform for IV applications.

This piece of technology, more than the visible components of the computer and videodisc player, is responsible for the growth and development of interactive video.

When the PC was launched a whole host of software was developed which suffered from varying and incompatible standards. The disc operating system (DOS) emerged as the standard operating system for the IBM PC and compatibles which meant that the microcomputer industry had a standard to which all software could be developed.

Much the same could be said for the IV industry with the development of the MIC — 2000 interface system from Videologic. The effect of the MIC — 2000 interface system on the IV industry has been likened to that of MS — DOS in the microcomputer industry.However while Microsoft and IBM are the sole suppliers of DOS, several other hardware manufacturers in the IV arena have produced competitive interface products.

Standardizing on the requirements of a hardware interface has enabled courseware to be written for IV applications without having to worry about the type of player, type of computer, input or output device. Hardware and software standards are to all intents and purposes transparent, which provides a suitable environment for software developers to work in.

There are basically two ways of combining graphics and video for IV purposes.

One way of superimposing graphics on video is for the interface board to output the separate PAL and RGB signals representing the video and graphics respectively. These signals, conveyed through a single cable, are then combined inside the display monitor using a method known as 'fast blanking'. Essentially, using this method, the display screen switches between the PAL video picture and the RGB graphics at such a fast rate that the illusion of graphics overlaid on video is created.

The second method takes advantage of state-of-the- art videodisc players, which supply the video signal as its components of red, green and blue along with the sync (RGBS). This method of transmitting the picture signal to the interface board allows for a much sharper image to be reproduced on the display screen. The graphics to be overlaid on the video image are generated as RGBS, which allows for the mixing of the video and the graphics to take place at board level since both sources are produced in the same way. This obviates the need for a fast blanking monitor since the monitor is fed only one signal, being the combination of video and graphics.

BUILDING THE IV SYSTEM

Assembling the appropriate delivery configuration begins with a clear perception of what the training programme is to achieve. It is crucial that the correct hardware elements are chosen, not only to satisfy the expected outcomes but also to ensure compatibility within the system itself. Some thought and investigation should be given to the physical components of an IV system, or it could prove to be wasted investment.

One important aspect which must be considered at this stage is software, for without the computer programs to drive the component parts there will be no IV system — just inert pieces of technology.

Hardware decisions are not independent of software considerations, indeed, here is true dependent partnership in every sense of the meaning since one cannot function without the other. Ideally the person or persons who will be implementing the software system should be involved at the initial stages in hardware decision making. In any case, the performance of the available software will be a criterion by which the hardware will be judged. So, before any capital investment is undertaken, it is vital to either take stock of the software facilities and talent at your disposal or thoroughly check software support for the system components.

The question of hardware, and software, compatibility for IV systems is of paramount importance. Answering the 'what works with what' query is no small task. As a system builder, the first task should be to identify the necessary components for the proposed system. Ideally this should be done at the outset of the project.

There are many IV hardware options on the market now, each with its own claim to uniqueness. No single company has a monopoly on any part of an IV system, so shopping around is an important and worthwhile task.

In circumstances like this, where new and advanced technology has to be assessed, there is no substitute for experience. Company or personal experience of IV systems is worth more than the reams of sales literature from manufacturers and suppliers.

At the very least you may be informed of what not to do. Many a costly mistake has been made in the investment of advanced technology based systems, which need relatively high up-front capital, because of the belief that problems can be solved with hardware. Much thought has to be put into the application of this new technology and the environment in which it is to operate.

Figure 7 Complete IV workstation

In practice there are two ways of arriving at a hardware system.

First, given that a an IV delivery system generally has a minimum specification of a microcomputer, videodisc player, display monitor and an interface which connects all the components together, there is the possibility of interchangeability throughout each of the system components. So it follows that a mix-and-match approach can be adopted and optimum performance can therefore be achieved from all parts of the system. In this way expansion to a system with, for example, voice cards or advanced graphics hardware can be catered for, and system components can be updated as enhancements, such as microprocessor development, become available. This method of assembly is best adopted where the intention is to use generic (general purpose) IV courses, or where there is the possibility of marketing the IV material which is to be developed.

The second method is to adopt a one-box solution. A complete IV workstation can be purchased from a single manufacturer or supplier, thus eliminating possible compatibility problems. Generally you would expect to pay a little bit extra for such a system. The drawback to this approach is in the dedication to a particular IV architecture. There may be no compatibility problems if new IV courseware is developed specifically for that system. However, should there come a time when the developed materials are to be sold to existing IV users there may be problems of portability.

Although most IV hardware systems are composed using the mix-and-match approach, this is not wholly an endorsement for that method, there are pros and cons to be weighed up for either route.

There has long been the need to stabilize and promote IV by identifying at least a minimum specification for those wishing to purchase a system on which generic courseware is to be run.

The absence of an agreed description has certainly had a braking effect on IV dissemination. However, after some discussion between the major generic producers in the IV industry, a common hardware specification, based on the IBM PC and laservision, has now been identified. The agreed hardware standard is irrespective of whether the hardware is bought as a complete delivery package or as individual parts. This minimum specification covers the basic elements of the system and, wherever possible, refrains from mentioning a specific manufacturer by name. We can now look in detail at the specifications for each dependent part of the system, before exploring the contents and capabilities of the single supplier, one-box system.

The computer

Up until now nothing much has been mentioned about the specifics of the computer to be used. In theory any type of computer that can communicate with a peripheral device could be used to control a videodisc player.

Although mainframe and minicomputers can and have been used in the past for computer-based training (CBT) materials, it is the huge amount of power and flexibility offered in one small box by the PC which sets it aside from the bigger and older members of the family. It is not necessary to fully understand the way in which a computer operates, but a basic grounding in the type and mode of operation in the computer used for IV purposes is desirable.

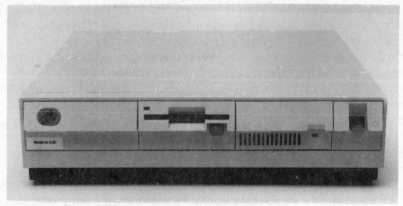

Figure 8 IBM PS/2 Computer

The heart of the PC is the microprocessor. These have developed at such a pace that the new generation of microprocessors such as Intel's 80386 and Motorola's 68020 chips outperform many mini and even mainframe installations.

The microprocessor chips now being offered to the PC user have in excess of a five-fold increase in speed from those of just three years ago.

The standard computer for IV delivery systems in the generic, off-the-shelf arena is the IBM PC. To be more specific, a PC/AT or compatible forms the basis from which potential users can base their computer needs. Of course the computer itself is made up of many, varied components and in order to equip the PC to the generic delivery station requirements the computer needs to be configured to a certain level.

The most important parts of the micro will be:

Part	Specification
Microprocessor	Intel 8088, 8086, 80286 or 80386 chip. No specific clock rate.
Operating system	PC — DOS or MS — DOS version 3.0 or later.
Random access memory	A minimum of 640K RAM.
Graphics adaptor	IBM or compatible enhanced graphics adaptor(EGA) with 256K onboard memory.
Disc drives	One hard disc drive with a minimum capacity for 20Mb of storage. One floppy disc drive — either 5.25" or 3.5" size with 1.2Mb of available storage.

Communications port   One serial port for asynchronous communications addressable as COM1.

Expansion slots   Desirable to have two available slots. One half-length (8 bit) slot for mouse or second communications port. A second full-length (16 bit) slot to allow for unspecified expansion.

Although the above definition is given with respect to IV systems which wish to be capable of running off-the-shelf productions, there are circumstances where this specification is not appropriate.

A different system may be based on a completely different computer such as the BBC Master, Amiga or Apple Macintosh, or even use the onboard intelligence of some videodisc players and thereby obviate the need for a powerful computer in simple applications.

The Commodore Amiga 2000, based on the powerful 32 bit Motorola 68000 microprocessor, is now being used for IV systems with the Microtext Authoring language and any professional laservision player. Apple have also made a significant push into the IV arena with the well received Hypercard software package to run on the Macintosh. Given the growing popularity of the Mac, this could be a significant development in IV.

Apple have also just launched a videodisc toolbox for the Mackintosh but at present two screens have to be used since the present screen cannot accept video pictures. It will be late 1988 or early 1989 before Apple will have a dual screen in the UK and then it will only be available on the Mac II system. However, given the growing popularity of the Mac, this could be a significant development in IV.

There are two main reasons for possibly straying from the identified standard. First, a large part of the existing hardware base has a lower specification, such as colour graphics (CGA) rather than enhanced graphics (EGA) capabilities or less storage capacity, than the agreed standard. The possibilities therefore available are for intended materials to be developed directly for that market, or for users to equip themselves only to use material available at the lower specification.

The second reason is that either users or producers may want to run or develop courses with a higher, perhaps more advanced, specification, which may include such extras as voice card, video digitizer, touch screen, frame store and so on. The extra, full-length, expansion slot included in the standard delivery micro is specifically there to accommodate this type of expansion.

There is a whole host of available computers which are capable of fulfilling the requirements of what is the hub of an IV system. Many computers can be fashioned to control a videodisc player, but the role of the computer in any reasonably advanced IV system is far more than that of a control device for a videodisc player.

In deciding what computer to use, the ultimate test is whether or not the computer is truly software and slot compatible with the IBM PC. If it is, you are unlikely to have generic courseware problems.

The IBM range of microcomputers which include the basic PC, XT, AT and the

PS2 model 30 are 100 per cent compatible. There are countless IBM clones and compatibles around and almost all should be problem free. Usable micros include those labelled: Compaq, Olivetti, Philips, Ferranti, Commodore, Ericsson, Zenith, Tandon, RM Nimbus AX, plus many more. Even some portables such as the Compaq portable can be used.

There are two fairly well known IBM compatibles, however, which do provide problems for inclusion in an IV system. The hardware solution which the Olivetti M24 PC uses to put information onto the display monitor may cause problems and only those with the indigenous display controller board are capable of being used. However, with constant development of hardware technology this may no longer be a problem. If an Olivetti M24 is to be used then it is advisable to seek advice in order to be completely sure.

The second, and better known compatible, where a problem exists is more clear cut. The Amstrad PC cannot be used in an IV configuration of any complexity. Commonly available, standard computer monitors cannot show video pictures and therefore a suitable monitor has to be used. For most PCs this is not a problem as monitors can be interchanged. For various reasons the Amstrad monitor cannot be separated from the computer box, chiefly because the monitor contains the PC power supply.

The main recommendation is to proceed along the 'middle of the road'. IBM PC compatible hardware is the safest bet for training systems. From this base you can add various options (such as voice cards) to the system while still retaining hardware flexibility.

It is becoming quite apparent that most IV training systems are being developed for the IBM PC and compatibles market or for the 'one-box' solution such as the Sony VIEW system. Although a standard IV system can be identified which provides guidelines, no one system has complete domination.

In the production of IV the costliest item is the preparation and design of the videodisc materials, which includes the video production process. Hardware components are becoming much more flexible and sophisticated and will continue to accommodate system variations in the future. So while a safety route exists for IV producers or users, there is still scope for experimentation on delivery systems for optimum performance in the presentation of an IV training package.

Computer to player communication

In order that the computer can control and interrogate the videodisc player an RS232—C interface connection is used. The player will usually be fitted with a male/female type adapter and, similarly ,the computer will either have a male or a female communications port. The RS232—C is a serial computer interface which conforms to international communications standards and the most economical method of peripheral control from a microcomputer.

Communication between the computer and the player generally follow the 'handshake' principle, where the player receives and responds to commands from the computer in the form of confirmation signals. The RS232 interface allows for two way communications between computer and player, which is often referred to as the full duplex mode of communication.

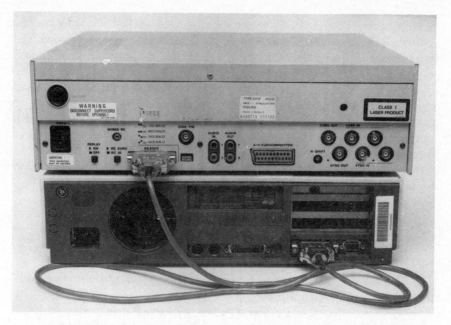

Figure 9 Rear of computer and player showing the RS232 cable link

The data transmission is usually preset at of 9600 baud. The baud rate is effectively the rate at which the computer sends commands to the player and receives the acknowledgements from the player.

All the information on the initial state of the computer and player along with the format of data is detailed in the operating instructions of the videodisc player. However, that information will not be necessary if an overlay card, the hardware interface sited in the computer, is used. The hardware interface will come supplied with the necessary cable connections, which will connect the RS232 — C ports of the computer and the player, and system software that will enable simple commands such as 'play' or 'eject' to activate the videodisc player.

The Player

The relationship between the videodisc player and the videodisc can be likened to that of the videotape player and the videotape. The difference is in the advanced optical techniques used in the operation of interactive videodisc systems, which results in much more powerful and flexible features.

In the domestic VHS videoplayer there will be, typically, between five and seven commands for controlling the videotape. Videodisc players, on the other hand, have a set of around 40 commands.

The manufacturers of videodisc players are tending to build players in the same way as any other computer peripheral would be constructed. The manufacturer will provide a list of functions available within the player and the method of executing these functions from a computer or computer-based control device. This means that most players will have as a minimum the RS232 — C connection, selectable baud rate and video-out and audio-out sockets. A PC can then be cabled to the player and, when both components are configured to the same baud rate, the computer can instruct the player to playback in a predetermined way.

In the future it is quite possible that players may benefit from the enormous and ever-increasing capabilities of the microprocessor. The present vogue of treating the player as a peripheral device of the computer may even be reversed, and all 'intelligence' could be housed within the player to which a suitable input device can be connected for interaction.

One example of the versatility of this playback medium is in the variety of ways in which the the footage on the videodisc can be displayed:

- Video — signal switched on or off;
- Play mode — normal or reverse;
- Speed rate — discrete steps allow setting of speed between still and scan forward;
- Still — still frame and step forward or reverse;
- Repeats — repeat segments or programmes repeatedly on completion;
- Access — typically around two seconds access to individual frame;
- Jump — instant jump between frames without loss of picture;
- Pause — on a frame for a specified time or indefinitely;
- Index — display frame numbers in any playback mode.

There are many other commands which enhance the presentation of material stored on an IV disc. All available players in the UK and Europe are designed to allow control of all its functions from an external computer and some allow control programs to be stored in an EPROM cartridge or the videodisc itself, to be loaded into the player's microprocessor for execution at playback time. The computer can also interrogate the videodisc player as to its current 'state', upon which the computer can take the appropriate action, if any.

Videodisc players are manufactured either for the NTSC market, which is largely the USA and Japan, or for the PAL market, which is largely the UK and most of Europe. The principal manufacturers, certainly for the PAL market, are Philips, Sony and Pioneer.

Philips led the IV level three applications market with their VP831 and VP835 models which were preceded by the now defunct 705 model. In fact none of these players are manufactured any more and Philips are now concentrating on what's known as the 400 series. Both Pioneer and Sony market PAL systems which are based on successful NTSC versions developed in the USA.

The VP835 series was introduced in 1984 with a range of models allowing for teletext encoding, EPROM cartridges, genlock and onboard CPU. A VP831 player also appeared as a scaled down version of the VP835. The VP705 player, which was based on the domestic model, was never used for any serious applications. Comments from the small group of VP705 users formed the basis for the VP835 player specification. Although no longer marketed, the rugged and 'tank-like' VP835 was the development player for many IV applications today, some of which are still in use.

Figure 10 Philips VP 410 videodisc player

Inevitably the optical technology which furnished the 1984 players is different to that in today's players. The types of lasers used have changed from the helium-neon type to a solid state laser producing an infra-red beam. Electronics is more in use and, overall, the entire optical system is more compact and efficient.

Another major new feature on some of today's players is the instant jump capability. When the laser has to move between, say, frames 1100 and 1150 there will be a momentary blank screen while the laser finds frame 1150. The effect is similar to that of a television programme ending and the advertisements appearing.

Instant jump moves the beam to frame 1150 without the blank screen, giving the appearance that frames 1100 and 1150 are consecutive. To accomplish this, the mirror which is pivoted to deflect the laser beam onto the videodisc is moved a certain degree which in effect 'flicks' the beam to the desired track and therefore the desired frame.

The Philips 400 series players were the first to incorporate an instant jump limit of +/- 50 frames while the newer Pioneer LDV4100 and the Sony LDP 1550P players claim limits of +/-200 and +/-100 respectively.

The range of models currently marketed are as follows, along with the telephone numbers under each company name:

Company	Model	Price £ (exc VAT)
Philips	VP405	1395
Tel: 01—689 2166	VP410	1795
	VP412	2695
	VP415	2995
Sony	LDP 1500	1195
Tel: 0784 67000	LDP1550P	1395

Pioneer	LDV4000	848
Tel: 01—575 5757	LDV4100	1150
	LDV6100	1777

Philips led the way in the manufacture of the new style front-loading players with the 400 series which includes the LV—ROM player (model 415) developed for the BBC Domesday project. A Genlock capability is standard on the Philips 410, 412 and 415 players, and can be included as an extra on the others. Genlocking allows two or more players to be linked together and the output from them both to be displayed on screen alternately. This is achieved by locking the sync pulses from the players for a smooth switch between each one.

The costliest player is not necessarily the most advanced. The Pioneer LDV4100 is the most advanced player in the Pioneer range but not the most expensive. The LDV6100 is similar to Philips 412 and 415 players in that it is a standalone player and can operate without an external computer. It has an ROM cartridge slot and as with the Philips 412 machine it can utilize a program dump from the videodisc or by a cartridge or even by a program previously downloaded from a computer.

For IV systems in a training environment the ideal players would seem to be Philips 410, Sony's 1550P and Pioneer's 4100. All have fast random access of around two seconds and employ instant jump. They are simply controlled by a computer and ideal for use with graphics overlay. The 1550P player from Sony has the widest instant jump facility of eight seconds, equivalent to 200 frames, which is a long time in an IV programme. It should therefore be possible to develop an IV programme which doesn't have any blank screens.

Sound is generally only available when the videodisc is playing in normal mode. However Pioneer's 4100 player claims sound production at speeds of up to +/- 10 per cent of normal speed. This could perhaps be useful for applications such as language learning.

Of course every player has its advantages and in order to find out which player accommodates specific needs, the best advice is simply to contact the various companies and peruse their technical literature.

The overlay system

An overlay system comprises of one or two expansion boards which plug into the rear of the PC. Any IBM PC and any 100 per cent compatible can be upgraded to a fully fledged IV system by installing this overlay facility and, if necessary, extra memory capacity . All that remains to be added to configure an IV system is the videodisc player and a display monitor.

From level two upwards this hardware interface allows hardware transparency and different computers, players, monitors and input devices can be configured with confidence.

Sited between the ever-developing hardware components, the overlay board will guarantee a consistent interface to the hardware and free the courseware and, perhaps more importantly, the software designer from the possibility of hardware incompatibility. Training courses can be designed and the accompanying computer software developed independently from the component pieces of hardware. Without doubt the development of this hardware interface has much to do with the very significant interest in the application of IV.

In the business and training sector the proliferation of the IBM microcomputer has dictated that most overlay boards are designed to operate in that environment. The conventional PC assembly has included the system box, monitor and keyboard. An upgraded IV system will include an overlay board (and graphics adaptor if necessary) housed inside the system box. The question then posed is how the interface permits hardware independence of, for example, the videodisc player? The short answer is computer software.

In the conventional computer configuration a number of devices have to be controlled: screen, disc drive, printer, keyboard and perhaps a mouse. To standardize communications between computer programs and these devices, the operating system is used.

The operating system for the IBM PC and compatibles is known as MS — DOS, also known as PC — DOS. The operating system is essentially a software layer between the computer hardware and the various devices, and within it are drivers for each device providing a simple method for any computer program to use any device. A simple example would be the use of the printer where access to it is basically the same irrespective of the computer program using it. The suppliers of the overlay system will provide a device driver which automatically becomes part of the operating system when the computer is switched on. Access is then gained to the functions of the overlay board including videodisc control and graphics generation in a simple and straightforward manner.

There may be slight differences in the actual implementation of the overlay system from supplier to supplier but the above description gives the basic idea behind the overlay operation.

Figure 11 Videologic MIC — 2000 interface system

The hardware interface could be chosen for all sorts of reasons but there is a minimal specification to which all overlay boards should meet in order to allow for a standard delivery system to be conceived:

- Resolution — minimum of 640 x 200 overlay resolution for graphics.
- Palette — minimum of 16 from 4096 colours.
- Transparency — any number of colours from 0 to all 16 should be redefinable as transparent to the video picture.-
- VPOS — the provision of vertical position (VPOS) of overlay graphics with respect to the video picture.
- Genlock — the screen should be stable at all times particularly during a search sequence.

Most overlay boards available for the IBM PC/PAL videodisc IV systems will satisfy the minimum requirements and many will provide additional features such as translucent colours, fading of video and/or graphics, along with other customized benefits.

There area number of overlay systems in IBM PC/PAL videodisc configurations, the best known of which are supplied by the following:

Company	System	Price £ (exc VAT)
Videologic Ltd. Tel: 09277 60511	MIC — 2000	975
	MIC — 3000	1325
	MIC — 3500	1425
VideoFusion Ltd. Tel: 0491 573388	Mixmaster EGA	950
Visage Information Systems Ltd. Tel: 0932 567222	V:Link 1602	1500
Cameron Communications . Ltd. Tel: 0734 664611	VideoMerge	1045
	VideoMerge RGB	1250
Wicat Systems Ltd. Tel: 0276 686186	PC Graphover II	1100
Appropriate Technology Ltd. Tel: 01—627 1000	Microkey/Mark 10	995
	Microkey/Mark 10 + RGB fader	1495
Transdata - KTS Ltd Tel: 01—251 8011	DVS - PC	1495

Since Philips, along with MCA in America, invented the videodisc player, and licence the standard to Sony and Pioneer, all overlay boards are compatible with the Philips models. This is a similar situation to the IBM PC and its compatibles, where the Philips players may not necessarily be the cheapest or the best but is the standard which future developments are based on. So if the overlay board is to work with a Sony or Pioneer player, then its worth checking on compatibility; in all probability both will be compatible.

Videologic dominate the British and European IV market for IBM PC/PAL videodisc systems They first launched the MIC — 2000 in September 1985 and it has really become the *de facto* standard for the hardware interface. However, competitive products are now beginning to make an impact with the demand for IV systems increasing rapidly. Indeed Videologic may yet find itself having the same relationship to the overlay market as IBM and Philips have to the computer and videodisc markets in the IV world.

All the various overlay boards boast some unique function and are continually developing new ones so before deciding on which particular board, it's best to telephone the suppliers for the very latest information.

The monitor

The display monitor in an IV system is a very important element. The clarity and sharp definition of the display is a learning motivation factor in training with IV. A special type of monitor is necessary because there is a need for both video and text, including graphics, to be displayed simultaneously on a single screen.

The word 'monitor' is used freely in reference to almost every type of display screen. Strictly speaking, a monitor is a screen which can display a pure video signal. This video signal has different characteristics to the signal received by a television fed from an aerial through a co-axial cable, as in a domestic VHS videotape set-up.

A standard television set cannot be used for IV display purposes. First, the resolution on a television set is not very good in comparison to that of a computer display. Text and graphics do not show up well on a television set.

Second, and more important, is the absence in most televisions of a what is known as a SCART connector. Without this connection a television set does not have access to all the range of signal inputs necessary to construct an IV screen. A SCART socket is a 21 pin Euroconnector which can carry a range of signals including RGB picture signals as well as control, synchronization and audio signals. Also, a standard television set needs the picture video signal superimposed on a radio carrier wave. It cannot deal with the video signal alone.

A standard computer display screen cannot be used for IV purposes. The simplified circuitry within a standard computer display is fed with only an RGB signal in digital or analogue form.

An IV monitor must be capable of showing both video and computer generated material together in a locked, steady, picture which must be as clear when static as when moving.

To achieve overlay of text and graphics, an 'interlaced' monitor must be used. A diagram of an interlaced screen is shown on page 36. In simple terms a television, and therefore video, picture is built up in lines at speeds designed to minimize flicker. For reasons explained previously, the lines are not transmitted consecutively but in an interlaced pattern, consisting of all the odd numbered lines followed by all the even numbered ones. A UK PAL formatted screen has 625 lines compared with the 525 lines of an American NTSC screen. Generally speaking, the more lines, the better the resolution.

Most modern computer terminals do not use interlacing. Interlacing monitors have to be used when both video and textual information are to be displayed concurrently and the video and computer signals have to be 'mixed' by special circuitry.

The most common method of overlaying text and graphics is by 'keying', also known as fast blanking. The monitor is fed both the composite video signal, which is the information relating to picture colour, brightness and so on, and the computer signal. The internal circuitry of the monitor is switched to 'black out' the video and the computer text is inserted. To achieve this satisfactorily the signal sources must be externally synchronized. This is known as genlock and ensures that the video and computer signals are in phase in order to hold the graphics steady on the screen. A monitor used for this function must have a 'fast blanking' capability.

There is another method of overlaying video which makes use of the latest technological developments of IV hardware.

The Philips 400 series of videodisc players transmit the picture information as components of RGBS, rather than composite video. Advanced overlay boards accept this RGBS signal, mix the computer information, and output a single RGBS signal to the monitor. This method takes advantage of the better picture quality in RGBS format as against the conventional composite video, which carries the deficiencies inherent in the PAL picture format. There is also no need for a fast- blanking monitor, therefore an increased range of monitors become available.

There are a number of quality monitors available for IV systems. The following is a sample of monitors with their prices accurate at November 1988:

COMPANY	MODEL	PRICE £ (exc VAT)
Microvitec	702	525
Tel: 0274 390011	604	795
	704	1195
	705	1149
Philips	8833	274
Tel: 01—689 2166	8873—05/BT	604
Sony	KX14CP1	590
Tel: 0784 67229	PUM2030	?
	PUM2730	?
Cameron Communications Ltd	Interact M	1875
Tel: 0734 664611	Pacer 33	1250
	Pacer 73	1600

The entire Cameron range have capacitance touch screens. Touch screens are described in more detail on page . It is possible to use them only as display monitors, albeit rather expensive ones.

The 700 series from Microvitec are also touch screens, with the 604 monitor having an upgrade kit available.

The two best selling monitors for IV are Sony's KX14CP1 and Philips CM 8833 medium resolution displays. The Pacer 33 touch screen based on the Philips 8833 monitor is also a medium resolution monitor. The Pacer 73 is based on the Philips CM 8873—05/BT monitor and has enhanced graphics resolution.

Three monitors take advantage of the high definition RGBS video signal from the Philips 440 series videodisc players, the Philips 8873 — 05/BT, Pacer 73 and the Microvitec 705.

Then audio functions within a monitor can vary somewhat between models. Some have extensive audio facilities and some require loudspeakers to be added to the monitor in order to produce sound.

This is not an exhaustive list of monitors and time should be taken to survey new ones which may have become available. It is a very important part of the system.

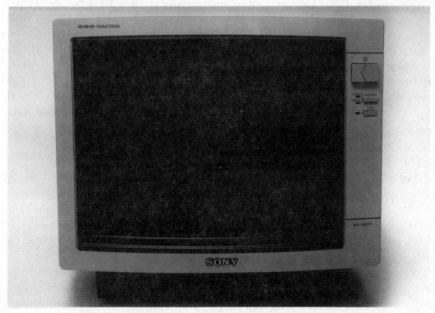

Figure 12 Sony KX14 CP1 Monitor

The input medium

One exciting aspect of IV is that it is not bound by conventional computer or conventional video thinking. A combination of both technologies requires a radical rethink to the design of programme content, software design and the method by which the user communicates with the system. The device which effectively links the user to the system is of paramount importance if the interactive nature of the system is to have any benefit. It follows that the input medium is an integral part of the programme specification. After all, there is not much use in employing a mouse if the input required is free-form answers.

How the various input devices work from a users viewpoint is elaborated upon on pages 105-106.

There are a number of input devices currently employed in IV applications, including:

- mouse
- tracker ball
- joystick
- light pen
- bar code reader
- touch sensitive screen
- keyboard.

The first three devices are similar in that they are referred to as pointing devices. A pointer moves freely around the screen in response to directional movements with the device, and a choice is made by pressing, usually, a button on the actual device. Software detects this button press and presents certain information to the applications program. These devices are relatively inexpensive and vary up to around £150. They can make a system less intimidating to a naive computer user.

By far the most common device of the first three is the mouse interface. The mouse is becoming more popular in all computer application areas, especially in systems such as the Apple Macintosh where graphics and windows are used to communicate with the computer rather than typed commands. In some computers a special port at the rear is used for such a pointing device. Another method for linking a pointing device to the computer is to connect the hardware via a standard RS232—C communications link.

For every input device, including the keyboard, there will more than likely be accompanying systems software to support it. Computer programs can interrogate this systems software, commonly a device driver, to determine whether an event has taken place and act accordingly. Computer programs can also be used to limit the scope of pointing device so that, for example, the only movement possible is from one menu item to another.

Two relatively uncommon IV input devices are the light-pen and bar-code reader. The light-pen has been used for a few applications and seems likely to be used for more if the Sony VIEW system is anything to go by, since it has included a light-pen slot in its computer. These devices operate in much the same way, technically, as the pointing devices, where software relays information on certain events.

The mouse, touch screen and keyboard are the most popular input mediums for IV, with the keyboard way out in front in terms of the number employed. However, the touch screen is finding increasing usage, especially in the point of sale and point of information applications. Certain training applications have also made use of the touch screen. The user interacts with the system by pressing his/her finger on a certain pre- determined part of the screen. Basically the co- ordinates of the interruption are transmitted to the computer program for interpretation and decision making.

A touch screen is capacitance or infra-red in nature.

The capacitance method is used by Cameron Communications for their touch screens used in IV, listed in the earlier section on monitors. The glass faceplate on the screen has a resistive coating which is fused to the glass. Software measures the position of the capacitive coupling when a finger touches the screen and the co-ordinates are transmitted to the computer via an RS232 — C cable link.

The infra-red method used by the Microvitec monitors employs infra-red beams which travel horizontally and vertically over the screen faceplate, from transmitters to sensors. When a finger touches the screen, the beam is interrupted, and the sensors calculate the co-ordinates, which are relayed back to the computer through the RS232 — C link. Although more expensive than the normal IV screen, the touch screen performs a dual function since it doubles as a display monitor and an input medium.

The most common and most flexible device is the standard keyboard. Usually the keyboard comes with the computer system unit and is usually the default input mechanism. The keyboard can be used to input text in the shape of free-form answers for digestion by the applications program. One touch entry can also be effected by using, for example, the function keys. Numbers can be used from the standard character set or from the now common, separate numerical keypad.

The input from a keyboard is first put into a temporary storage area known as a buffer. The applications program can interrogate the buffer to find out if input is available without committing itself to taking the input and therefore be forced to make some kind of decision. The program can flush the buffer if the contents are not relevant and also disable part, or all, of the keyboard as and when it wishes.

Of course, it is possible to combine input devices. In these situations there is usually a keyboard and another input device such as a light-pen reader. Technically, this doesn't cause any major problems but it may be rather confusing to the user.

Other types of input devices, such as the concept keyboard where there are only a minimal amount of keys which initiate operations rather than generate a single character, are gaining popularity and no doubt applications will be developed for this and other new devices.

The voice card

Although a voice card isn't part of a conventional IV set up at present, it does merit some thought as to the advantages that external, digital, audio could bring to an IV situation.

Speech technology is certainly an area where major activity is taking place and will continue to develop with time. However, speech recognition has not yet developed to such an extent where it can be usefully employed in IV training programmes, but this is not the reason for considering an audio board.

There are perhaps two reasons for considering audio support. The first is simply to augment existing CBT materials. New and existing packages could be developed with the voice card and quality graphics to provide a supplement to IV material. Benefits include the fact that audio can be constantly updated as, unlike audio on a videodisc, it is not 'cast in stone'.

This leads on to the second reason. Audio over still frame has long been a problem with current IV, although the technology of laservision has tried to overcome this. However, there is still no flexible and cost effective way of producing it. Audio is only available from the videodisc when the video is playing.

A voice card enables the storing, editing and playback of 'flexible' audio in an IV package. Digitized audio can be stored in files on a floppy or hard disc, updated at any time and incorporated into IV applications programmes.

The basic hardware involved is:
- a full length IBM PC compatible board
- a microphone
- a speaker
- cables and software

Voice cards vary in price from under £300 for the Audiocard 300 from STC Mercator in Great Yarmouth (Tel: 0493 844911), to the top-of-the-range model, the Votan VPC2140 card from VSI of Cambridge (Tel: 0223 862327), which retails for around £2000. There is a big difference in the quality of the audio facilities offered from these cards reflected by the fact that the Votan card stores audio at a rate of around 2KBytes per second compared with 4KBytes per second offered by the Audiocard 300.

Voice cards are being developed by varying manufacturers as they perceive the benefits in production. Visage, who make an IV overlay board, have a digital audio board which has been available since October 1987. The V:Link 1800 Digital Audio Board can be fully integrated into an IV package.

Videodisc audio, as well as other sources of audio, can be routed through the card. The load on the computer's CPU is lightened by two onboard, independent processors. One functions to control the operation of the card and also communications with the computer. The other handles the compression and digital filtering of the audio.

There are also three fidelity modes which can be selected under software control. These are:
- (1) High-quality (10 KBytes/second)
- (2) Music   (6.5 KBytes/second)
- (3) Speech   (3 KBytes/second)

Visage Information Systems (Tel: 0932 567222) supply the card at £950.

There are many more facilities, such as editing recorded speech, which this and other voice cards offer, under software control, to the IV environment.

The complete system

Although standardization has solved many of the compatibility issues that beset IV in its formative years, to some, building a system can prove problematic. There are at least four components which have to be assembled together for any serious training system.

Standards, coupled with an open architecture approach in the computing industry, have made it a relatively simple task to physically build a system from different suppliers. However, dealing with potentially four different manufacturers may become a real headache! One way of avoiding this is to make a third party, perhaps an agent or dealer, responsible for putting together the system. Another is to plump for a one-box solution, in which case a single manufacturer will supply the entire system.

A fully integrated one-box solution is the response to a demand for simple yet powerful IV systems. At this point the difference between a single supplier and a single manufacturer should be pointed out. A single supplier will use other manufacturers' equipment for part, or whole, of a system, whereas a single manufacturer produces and combines all the components of the system under their brand name. Only Philips, Sony and Pioneer, who manufacture the PAL players for the UK and European markets, have the possibility of being single manufacturers. In fact the only true single manufacturer to date is Sony.

The complete-system approach appeals to companies who perceive the great advantages of IV but do not have the time or technical expertise to devote to installing the system.

Most companies who manufacture at least one component in an IV kit can now quote customers for the delivery of a complete system. Another headache relieved is that of backup service and maintenance. If a fault occurs then it is much easier to deal with one company than contact four in an effort to find out what is causing the problem.

The major problem of buying a single manufacturer's system is that you may be locked into using software which only works with the given hardware.

The Sony VIEW system could be a potential source of problems in this area. However Sony have wisely taken steps to avert this by emulating Videologic's MIC environment, the common overlay standard, thus giving access to a wide generic base of IV applications already available. This should also ensure future compatibility with new packages.

While Sony's VIEW system is the only single manufacturer's system, Philip's offerings include one essential part from another manufacturer. The Philips IV workstation uses Videologic's MIC IVA 2000 overlay board in its configuration. This is quite a shrewd move since most existing training applications use the Philips/Videologic components in their system and Philips IV workstations reinforce this partnership. Sony, on the other hand, have been forced to emulate the MIC system in order to compete.

The Sony VIEW workstation comes in two formats, the difference being the player used in the configuration. VIEW/1 uses the 1500P player while VIEW/2 uses the 1550P player which accounts for the latter being more expensive. The specification for the VIEW system is:

- SMC — 3000VP PC AT compatible with:
        40 MByte hard disc drive
        1.44 MByte floppy disc drive (3.5 inch)
        CGA card
        Sony Hi-resolution Graphics card
        2 x RS232 communication ports (9 pin)
        Printer port

Light-pen port
IBM PCAT compatible keyboard
System cables
MS — DOS version 3.2

- LDP 1500P videodisc player for VIEW/1
- LDP 1550P videodisc player for VIEW/2
- KX14CP1 14" Trinitron monitor.

Total system price for: VIEW/1   £5795
                         VIEW/2   £5995.

Philips offer two workstation models, the 312033 and 322033 specifications. As with the Sony VIEW system, there is only one difference between the systems. On this occasion it is the computer. Philip's specifications are as follows:
- P3105 PC XT compatible for Model 312033
- P32202 PC AT compatible for Model 322033
          20 Mbyte hard disc drive
          640K RAM
          MIC IVA 2000 overlay card
          EGA card
          Communication port
          Printer port
          PC XT/AT compatible keyboard
          System cables
- VP405 videodisc player
- Philips 8833 14" monitor

Total system price for: Model 312033   £3995
                          Model 322033   £5300

Other suppliers are now putting together systems in order to satisfy a growing demand for complete workstations. Microvitec, better known for their range of monitors, are one such company who now offer a range of complete workstations. The specifications for each are:

Microvitec Insight One: -
          - IBM PC compatible computer
                    single 5.25 inch floppy disc drive
                    640K RAM
                    MIC IVA 2000 overlay board
                    CGA card
                    Communications port
                    Printer port
                    PC compatible keyboard
                    System support software

- Pioneer LDV4100 videodisc player
- Microvitec 702 14" monitor

Optional extras include digital audio, second disc drive for computer and a mouse.

Total system price: £4200

Microvitec Insight Two:
-   Similar computer to workstation one but with the following additions/substi-
    tutes:
20 Mbyte hard disc
EGA card
Microvitec 604 15" FFT monitor

Total system price: £4500

Microvitec Insight Three:
- An 80286 based PC AT compatible with:
          30 MByte hard disc drive
          1.2 MByte floppy disc drive
          1 MByte RAM
          MIC IVA 3000 overlay card
          EGA card
          PC AT compatible keyboard
          Mouse
          Systems software support

- Pioneer LDV4100 videodisc player
- Microvitec 15" touch screen

Total system price: £5900

All manufacturers and suppliers reserve the right to alter their configurations
without prior notice, so if a one-box solution appeals to you then ring the manufac-
turer/supplier for the up-to-date details. If a one-box solution is to be used then a good
way to measure its compatibility with current and future IV programmes is to check
that it has at least the minimum specifications of the laservision standard, and the
operating s andards of the computer and overlay system laid out in the appropriate
section earl er in this chapter.

OPTICAL DISC TECHNOLOGY

There is no doubt that optical disc storage in its various incarnations — from the videodisc through the compact disc and digital optical recording — is the technology of the time. Although, in commercial terms, it is less than ten years old, optical disc technology has been responsible for two revolutionary developments; interactive video and the most successful innovation in consumer electronics ever, CD—audio.

In fact the evolutionary development of the optical disc stretches back to the late sixties when, with the laser having been invented, Philips began to to focus on the possibility of optical storage utilizing the precision and high resolution of the laser beam.

Judging by the level of investment which has been, and continues to be, expended into the research and development of optical technology there is a likelihood that the impact of this new communications and mass storage medium will have considerable effect in both our work life and our leisure time activities.

Like the early days of the microcomputer, the optical storage arena has a confusing proliferation of standards and acronyms, chief amongst which are:

CD — A   : compact disc — audio
CD — ROM   : compact disc — read only memory
LV — ROM   : laservision — read only memory
CD — V   : compact disc — video
CD — I   : compact disc — interactive
DVI   : digital video interactive
ICVD   : interactive compact video disc

These may be obscure technologies to some. However, these developing standards in optical disc technology, which are either in the market place now or set to become commercial realities in the near future, will shape the future of information storage and manipulation in all spheres of life in 1990's and beyond.

With limitless applications the future for the optical disc industry looks very bright. Interactive video in particular will continue to develop and become the standard delivery system for effective training. However, unlike the computer industry, which now has the micro standard in the IBM PC, optical storage has no universal standard and is thus typified by a battery of disc sizes. This undoubtedly has a stifling effect on sales, which, although sizeable at present, could be greatly expanded by the major optical disc manufacturers agreeing on worldwide standards.

The history of confusion began as soon as Philips demonstrated the first videodiscs around 1972/73. MCA in the US and a list of Japanese companies began to develop similar technology. The domestic market has been the great beneficiary of an agreement for optical disc standards.

In 1979, one year after Philips defined what is probably the most familiar method of optical storage, the compact disc system, an agreement was struck between Philips and Sony with the aim of establishing CD as the world standard for digital audio discs. The first commercial CD player was launched in 1982 and the rest is history : some 10 million CD players and well over 100 million discs had been sold worldwide by the end of 1986 and the sales trend is continuing to increase rapidly.

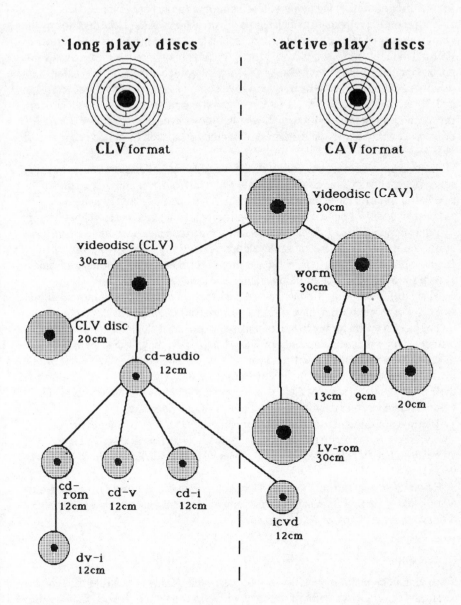

Figure 13 The optical family tree

There are two developments which have been, and will continue to be, extremely beneficial to the IV community.

Firstly, due to the recognized clutter of disc sizes and standards the major manufacturers are now addressing themselves to the disc player problem. The most notable are the Philips 'Combi' players, launched in 1988 which will play all the CD format discs as well as the larger videodisc formats anywhere in the world.

The second development, which has been a great boost to IV, is the decision by the manufacturers of interactive videodiscs to standardize on the laservision format of Philips. In reality the 30cm videodisc used for IV applications has meant that IV has not been subject to the varying standards of optical storage in the same way as the more recent optical disc developments which have come in various sizes of between 9cm and 30cm in diameter. There is one very good reason for this. All optical discs, irrespective of their dimensions and whether they have been developed for audio, broadcast quality television pictures or computer data, stem from one origin — the videodisc.

There is the very real possibility of the erasable optical disc becoming a reality soon. Optical discs which can be written to and read from over and over again will be a powerful force for the penetration of optical disc technology, although it may not be as beneficial for IV applications as for applications such as database and publishing.

While new optical disc developments will serve to enhance interactive video, there is no doubt that IV is the most developed and widely used of the optical disc technologies in the industrial market. It provides trainers with the most advanced system for the automation of training and basic knowledge transfer.

Many different forms of optical disc technology, in terms of analogue and digital as well as size and format, have originated from the videodisc development.

The most relevant format to the training sector are the developments along the CD format. The published standards of CD—I and DVI, reckoned to be the closest relations to IV in compact disc format, are not yet commercial products and it will be in the 1990s before we see if the reality lives up to the hype. Philips, who published the CD—I standard, say that there is no competition between the formats, as CD—I can in no way compete with the video power of the videodisc.

There is no doubting that uncertainties are caused, and problems of decision compounded, by the premature hype of developments such as CD—I, DVI and ICVD especially since there is already confusion over what is available now, let alone in five years time.

However an overview of the related technologies in the compact disc arena is still worthwhile since they represent a further convergence of the computing and optical disc technologies into one delivery source.

CD—Audio

Since its launch in 1983 the CD—A disc has revolutionized the world of recorded music and set a new standard for sound reproduction quality. Compact disc — audio was the first application of the CD principle developed jointly by Philips and Sony.

The standard has tapped a worldwide market. The success of CD technology is mainly due to this partnership of Philips and Sony. Sony's experience of digital recording allied to Philips expertise in electronic and optical disc technology, largely gained from laservision, combined into a powerful development force.

The current CD—A discs play 74 minutes of top quality, digitally encoded, sound on a 12cm CLV disc. Licensed to other manufacturers, the optical readout method guarantees an everlasting product with no degradation in quality with age.

Playing the disc requires a special CD— Audio player. However, the penetration of this system in the home market has been phenomenal, and extended global success is assured.

Distinct from the 30cm analogue LP record, the CD—A disc spins at between 500 — 200 rpm compared with 33 1/3 rpm of an LP record. Also available on the CD player is a facility permitting the selection of available music to be played in any order.

Without laservision there would have been no CD—A, without which it is doubtful whether the rush of CD formats would have come about.

Although itself not relevant to the business and training sectors of the economy, CD—DA was the first real test of optical disc technology as a fully blown consumer product. Undoubtedly the acceptance of the technology in the domestic market has been the propellant for the development of the newer CD formats for many differing applications.

CD — ROM

A CD—ROM disc is similar in type to that used for CD—A, the difference being that the information is read by the computer rather than being converted into audio signals.

This was the second CD format, introduced in 1985 by the Philips/Sony partnership. CD—ROM is used mainly for the storage and retrieval of fixed information. Information distribution, publishing and large database handling are key application areas for CD— ROM, with random access over the dense volume of data with an inconceivable degree of accuracy

The validity of the CD—ROM approach to these key application areas is becoming more apparent as the the cost of replicating discs rapidly declines. To date there are no known entertainment or training applications available in CD—ROM format.

A development of 12cm CD—ROM and the 30cm videodisc is the 30cm LV— ROM format. Developed by Philips, this format combines the analogue video with digital data stored in the audio channel or analogue audio itself. LV—ROM is the basis for the Domesday system, sometimes referred to as advanced interactive video (AIV). AIV was developed by Philips in conjunction with the BBC and is dedicated to a BBC microcomputer environment, although Logica has produced software for the IBM PC environment.

A CD—ROM system is configured in much the same way as a conventional computer set up — computer, screen, disc drives, keyboard — with the addition of an optical disc drive, with the dimensions of a 5 inch floppy disc drive, as well as or in place of a magnetic disc drive. The disc itself is a high volume digital data storage medium capable of containing 600 megabytes of information on one 12cm CLV disc. This is equivalent to 1500 floppy discs or around 250 000 pages of text! As with all optical disc drives, the protective perspex coating and the use of the optical readout method, ensures that the information inside the disc is completely protected for, theoretically, all time.

Actually a CD—ROM disc is designed to store any information — text, graphics, video, audio — which can be digitally encoded. However it is expensive in digital storage terms to encode video on a digital optical disc so the usual CD—ROM disc will contain data and graphics for computer use.

CD—Video

After a relatively long incubation, Philips have launched a new kind of 12cm compact disc which stores five minutes of analogue video, with accompanying digital sound, along with 20 minutes of digital sound—only.

CD—V merges the sound capabilities of the CD—A disc with the top-quality analogue video of the laservision videodisc into a single audiovisual entertainment system for the domestic market. These CD—V discs will not only be reproduced in 12cm size but also in 20cm and 30cm sizes. The latter being the same size as the IV disc. These different sizes offer the customer between five minutes and two hours of video and sound. The 30cm CD—V disc is a boost to the IV industry since to accommodate the differing CD formats and optical disc sizes, Philips have developed the 'Combi' player which is capable of playing all disc sizes including the 30cm CAV disc.

In contrast to the other CD formats, CD—V information is held in analogue form rather than digital.

The reason for analogue is the amount of space necessary to store digitized video signals. Typical CD—A discs spin inside the player at a speed between 500rpm and 200rpm. At this speed digital data is retrieved from the disc at 4.3Mb per second. This is far to slow to reproduce 25 or 30 colour television pictures per second. The rotational speed is increased for the analogue video and its accompanying digital sound. Also the video, with its sound, is encoded at the outer edge of the disc with the innermost part being used for 20 minutes of CD—A quality audio. For CD—V discs in the PAL format, the speed is increased in range to 2250rpm and 1512rpm with NTSC type discs spinning between 2700rpm and 1815rpm. These speeds allow for the laser scanning speed to be sufficient to transfer the video and digital information.

You may have already deduced that there are a couple of potential incompatibility issues to be addressed with CD—V discs.

First, CD—V is encoded in analogue rather than digital form and has a different scanning speed to the other CD type discs, so a CD—V disc cannot be played on a CD—A player. To be more precise, the 20 minutes of audio—only will play but the 5 minutes of video and sound will not. Eventually two types of players will probably be sold. One for the 12cm CD—V discs, which will probably play CD—A discs and retail for under £400. The second will be the 'combi' player which will be able to play all the optical discs and retail for around £500. The influential Japanese firms (Sony, Pioneer, Matsushita, Hitachi and Yamaha) have pledged support for the 'combi' system and will develop similar players.

The second problem is the more intractable one in that CD—V is tied to the TV standards of PAL and NTSC. This is definitely CD—V's biggest drawback.

Although CD—V is not a worldwide standard the quality of the material is quite apparent and capitalising on CD—A and also with the support of the music industry it seems likely that this will be another success story for the optical CD industry.

CD—Interactive

Of all the CD formats which Philips and Sony have announced, the CD — I specification has aroused the biggest response. Certainly it is causing ripples in the IV industry, not least because it is the first CD format which encroaches on the domain normally associated with IV.

The intention to develop CD—I was made jointly by Philips and Sony in March 1986; it is likely that systems willbe available in the USA by Spring 1989, with a major launch in time for Christmas 1989. This means that the UK will probably see a complete CD—I system in early 1990.

CD—I has been billed as the most powerful medium yet to deliver education and entertainment to initially the domestic consumer but ultimately to the professional sector as well. If the reality lives up to the hype then there is a real possibility that CD—I will tap worldwide markets and be at least as successful as CD—DA. Philips certainly believe that this could be the case.

The document containing the complete international specification, known as the green book, offers both a delivery medium standard as well as a product standard. This extensive specification will be to the benefit of producers and consumers alike.

The problem at the moment is that few people have actually had the opportunity to independently assess the medium. No fully fledged system has yet been bench-tested.

Like all the CD formats, the disc diameter is 12cm and rotates at a speed in the range 500—200rpm. In fact all CD discs have the same dimensions and, with the exception of CD—V discs, use the digital encoding method. The difference is in the way in which the information on the disc is interpreted.

The capacity of the disc allows for 600Mb of computer data or 72 minutes of CD—DA quality audio or 6000 pictures or any combination of these features. The versatility of the medium is demonstrated, not only in the on screen fusion of the different components — audio, video, text and graphics, but in the ability to deliver these individual components in a variety of ways. Taking video as an example, there is a choice of three levels of resolution: normal (equivalent to the resolution on a current TV set), double (equivalent to a computer monitor), and high (double normal resolution in vertical and horizontal directions).

The video effects possible include wipes, dissolves and transparency, using two image planes, which provide for more interesting, dynamic and more interactive images. The same versatility applies to the audio component where the distinct levels of quality are LP record, FM radio, AM radio and telephone.

With the applications program and data also resident on the disc, CD—I may be the first genuine multimedia information disc.

The hardware to run the programme disc will be straightforward, yet very powerful. There will be a CD—I player and probably some sort of keyboard or mouse to be plugged into a standard TV set.

All the consumer will have to do is switch on the player and the TV set, put in the disc and he or she will be presented with an interactive programme.

By closely defining both hardware and software elements the CI system is essentially a black box, 'closed architecture' system with standard video and audio, and probably computer, connections. This allows for a household to buy a CD—I player, and plug it into their TV set, anywhere in the world and play a CD—I disc.

CD—I does have shortcomings. The major problem is that it cannot play back full screen, full motion, moving pictures.

This is a major benefit that IV has over CD—I. The medium wasn't initially created for moving video but more for animation, and besides, CD digital optical storage doesn't have the capacity to store moving video economically as yet. This is why CD—V has an analogue format. However, research is ongoing to find technically and economically viable video compression techniques for future developments in CD—I.

IV has superior moving video capabilities and more flexible interactive computer control than CD—I. However, there is no doubt that the concept of CD—I is very attractive and if Philips and Sony get the marketing right, and develop the technology, then CD—I could be the CD flagship and encroach into the domain of IV in years to come.

DV—Interactive

Digital video interactive is a technology developed in the USA to allow full motion video to be stored on a CD—ROM disc as well as audio, text and computer graphics.

DV—I was developed by General Electric (GE) at the David Sarnoff Research Centre (formerly RCA laboratories) in New Jersey, USA. Essentially DV—I takes advantage of the digital storage capacity of the CD—ROM disc to provide over 60 minutes of full motion video.

Comparisons have been made between DV—I and CD—I, with the odd reference to IV thrown in as well. But there is one important difference: CD—I is a specification for a complete system, hardware and software, whereas DV—I is a technology based on computer chips which deliver previously compressed video and audio from a compact disc, in real time. DV—I needs an IBM PCAT or compatible and a CD—ROM drive.

DV—I hasn't had the pomp and circumstance that surrounded the development of CD—I, but a close look at the technology suggests that this is a very significant development in digital video encoding. Without DV—I technology, CD—ROM discs are capable of storing only 30 seconds of moving video, as compared with over one hour if DV—I technology is used.

The solution DV—I has taken to the the problem of too much video information and not enough storage capacity is a powerful compression/decompression system. Before being committed to a CD—ROM disc, the video and audio are compressed so that fewer digital bits are necessary to represent the required video and audio.

When the CD—ROM disc is used and the video and audio material played back, the compressed information must be decompressed in order to reconstitute the original and video material. This decompression has to be done in real time. Basically this means that the D —I computer boards, housed in the expansion slots of the PC, have to decompress the material coming from the CD—ROM disc each time the disc played. Whereas the decompression technique has to be performed as the disc is playing, the actual compression of the video and audio material onto the CDᵉ—ROM disc only has to be carried out once, before the information is committed to disc.

DV—I is a technology rather than a complete system.

The main requirements for a system are an IBM PCAT or compatible and a CD—ROM device. DV—I technology resides on computer boards which plug into the expansion slots of an IBM PCAT. The base system requires two boards, a video and an audio board. These boards perform the real time decompression of video and audio and permit special effects to be used with the digitized material. A third board is available as an add-on, which contains the CD—ROM interface supported by additional memory and joystick, and probably other input device.

Since it is IBM PC based, initial applications will be targeted to the professional market, launched in the USA in 1988. Consumer markets are the long- term aim and large investment is required in cost reduction, manufacturing and marketing, which means that it is unlikely that a consumer product will be available until at least 1990.

ICVD

Interactive compact video disc (ICVD) is the latest compact disc format to emerge from the USA. The new system was developed in California by Lowell Noble of SOCS Research Incorporated.

As with all the CD formats, an ICVD disc measures 12cm in diameter. Unlike the other CD formats ICVD material can be encoded in the interactive, CAV format.

ICVD will offer 12 or 20 minutes of video and digital audio, depending of whether the material is encoded in the CLV or the CAV format. It will have a playing time of 20 minutes if the material is laid out in the linear CLV format. However, the interactive, still frame capabilities of the CAV format can be used, which reduces the total playing time to 12 minutes. Video material on the disc is encoded in analogue while the sound is digitally recorded.

ICVD players, which should start appearing in early 1989 and retail for around £200, will be able to play the existing CD formats of CD—A and CD—ROM. A claim is also made that the players will accept discs encoded for DV—I technology.

The interesting aspects of ICVD are the amount of playing time offered and the CAV format which allows for interactive facilities.

Interactive possibilities emerge from ICVD from material stored in the CAV format. Although seen as competition to CD—Video, ICVD uses similar technology, apart from the digitally encoded audio, to that of laservision. ICVD could be viewed as the videodisc shrunk from 30cm to 12cm. Perhaps interactive applications will develop from ICVD in 12cm discs, with 12 minutes of video, as well as the 30cm videodisc which has the capacity for 72 minutes of video and sound on a double sided disc.

It is not unlikely that Philips will develop the combined formats of CD and laservision along those of ICVD.

Apart from CD—A and CD—ROM none of the emerging CD technologies has actually fully arrived in the market place. The optical pundits have been giving their hypothesis on the CD struggle since 1986 and it now looks likely that 1989/1990 will be the battleground of the 'format-wars' when the users enter the arena.

Chapter 3

VIDEO AND FILM

MAKING PROGRAMMES

Thinking clearly

Interactive video is different. It's the only application so far devised which requires more than passive participation from the viewer — hence the name. It's radically different from the tapes you hire from your local video library, or buy from the programme makers or their distributors. You don't just sit there and watch it — you have to participate.

It's different technically, as well. It starts with the same kind of tape used by television programme makers, or a similar tape recording system, and it finishes on a video disc.

The equipment necessary is expensive. It's vastly superior to your home video recorder, but you have to pay for the superiority. And the programmes are expensive to produce. All television or video programmes are expensive to produce. A great deal of skill and experience go into the making of them and the production process is both complicated and lengthy. The producers recover their expenditure — and make their profits — from the audiences who watch their programmes, which are numbered in millions.

But interactive video programmes are designed to be used by individuals. Perhaps a programme will be used by several hundred individuals, but they are not aimed at mass audiences. Therefore the cost cannot be recovered from the audiences.

So the first decision to be made when contemplating the making of an interactive video programme is whether or not one is necessary. What the programmes do supremely well is perform teaching and training functions.

If the decision is that the best way of achieving an objective is with an interactive video programme, the next sensible step is to see whether or not an existing programme is suitable. Then, if a suitable programme is found, to see whether or not it is available and, if it is, at what cost. During this process, it's possible that you'll come across a programme that would suit your purpose if it were adapted. The prudent thing to do then, is to ask the owners if they would give permission for the adaptation and to enquire as to the cost.

If your investigations show that no existing programme is suitable, even with adaptation, you'll need to start the process of making one, or having one made. When that process is complete, you'll have bought something that is technically excellent. Press the right buttons and you'll get the right responses, unfailingly. But what you see on the screen will be only as good, or as bad, as the programme material that was created for your system.

There'll be pictures and there'll be sounds. But whether or not they put over the messages you intended will depend entirely on the skill with which the video programme was made. It is not possible to guarantee excellence in programme production. You can hire all the right people and they can do all the right things, and the finished product may still not be right.

No producer aspires to achieve boredom, but the danger that the production will fail is always there. In interactive video programmes the danger of boredom is greater than in other programmes. The material is repeated time and time again. Any flaw will be exaggerated by the constant repetition.

Although the repetition of the programme material is a distinct disadvantage, there is a major advantage to be set against it. If the purpose of an interactive video programme is to educate or to train, the objectives of the programme are more capable of precise definition than those of programmes intended for mass audiences which demand entertainment.

It is, of course, desirable, that interactive video programmes be interesting and, if possible, entertaining. But the audience for which they are intended is made up of individuals with a commitment to acquiring the information contained in a particular programme. That commitment may be a natural one, or it may be induced. But it is there, at least to the extent that the individuals are prepared to participate.

So you have what amounts to almost a captive audience, an audience willing to take part in the learning process, whatever it may be. But it is possible to alienate even a captive audience, if the individuals who make it up find that their expectations are not being realized. You have to give them what they expect. And to do that it is vital to take the greatest possible care over the planning and execution of the programme.

Planning programmes

The essential first stage in the process of planning a programme is to decide on the objectives you seek to achieve. In this case the overall objective is to educate, or to train, or both. But an overall objective is by no means good enough. The more general the objective, the more likely it is that it will not be achieved. The chances of success are far greater if the overall objective is analysed clearly, agreed with all concerned and, eventually, stated in precise terms.

The next stage is to split the overall objective into as many stages as is reasonable This leads, inevitably, to a series of objectives. This is the time to make sure that the stages start at the logical beginning and follow a sensible progression until they arrive at a satisfactory conclusion.

While you are undertaking this process, it's as well to ask yourself again whether or not you should be making an interactive video programme. The number of objectives you've set, and the nature of them, will give you some idea of the complexity of the project. It may be difficult to complete satisfactorily, and complications lead to expense. The total costs involved may exceed the money available.

Assuming that you decide to continue, you should use your list of objectives to start planning your programme.

The next stage requires imagination. You consider the first objective and you imagine ways in which it might be achieved. The possibilities are numerous. Assume that the programme you are making is a programme which trains an individual to make an interactive video programme. You have decided that the programme will open by showing what can be achieved with such programmes.

It's an interactive programme you're making, so the individual using it must be able to participate, not just sit and watch. The participation involved could only be the ability to rerun the sequence as many times as the participator wants to run it. So you could start with someone talking to camera and delivering an exposition. In a way that's the simplest start possible, and there's much to be said in favour of keeping things simple. But it may not be the most effective start possible, and it may not be the best way of ensuring that the viewer assimilates the information you are delivering. The advantage of video over audio is that pictures are far more easily remembered than words. So, it's desirable to aim for a sequence of memorable pictures. Then, if the viewer is offered a number of options, he or she is likely to find the interactive process more interesting.

So, you aim for a sequence of memorable pictures — and appropriate sounds — and a number of interactive options. The next stage is to create the pictures and decide on the options that are to be available to the participator.

Getting pictures

There are two basic ways of getting pictures. One is to originate them yourself, or commission someone to do it for you. The other is to use existing pictures from whatever sources are available If you decide that you're going to originate yourself, there's a good chance that you may get something that will suit your purpose.

Success is not inevitable, because programme-making is an art not a science. But it follows that if someone of talent has already recorded the images you wish to use, it could be foolish to decide to start from scratch yourself.

It's time to move on from the example of making an interactive video programme about how to make an interactive video programme, if only because few, if any, talented artists, or craftspeople, have tackled the task. It could well be that it's an appropriate subject for an interactive programme. But for the programme you are making, whatever the subject, you could need a sequence that someone else has made already. Imagine that you need a sequence showing a rocket being launched into space. It would be possible to commission coverage of such a launch, but the cost would be enormous. The alternative is to approach a television company for a copy of an appropriate sequence.

The first problem you'll meet is the bureaucratic fudge you're likely to encounter — television companies do not see it as one of their prime functions to provide sequences for other programme makers Then, you may need all kinds of permissions from copyright holders. Then the television company is likely to levy what it considers to be a nominal charge for the material. And that nominal charge could well run into hundreds if not thousands of pounds.

If, because you are an imaginative and resourceful individual, you're considering recording a sequence off the next relevant transmission, don't do it. Recording so that you can watch something at your own convenience is not illegal. Even if it were, no-one is likely to take action against you. But recording something for any other use, including for an interactive programme, is illegal, and the danger of being punished if you break the law in this respect is real. Nevertheless, it is possible to get permission to use existing sequences and it is not inevitable that the costs should be unaffordable.

If you decide that you are going to originate your opening sequence, then you are approaching the start of the programme making process.Every stage in that process will require as much care and as much thought as did the preliminary stage. You will need to spend as much time over each succeeding sequence as was necessary for the opening sequence. And you must remember that it may be necessary for one sequence to flow into another, rather than to stand entirely separate from it.

The important point to remember is that it could well take longer to devise and plan a programme than it does to realize it. And while you're struggling with the process, you could well make the sensible decision that you're not capable of finishing it successfully. If you believe still that you need an interactive video programme, this is the time when you may decide to hire a producer.

Having taken that decision, your problems have not disappeared. The programme you get, ultimately, from the producer will only be as good as the briefing you give him.

Whether you're briefing a producer or continuing the planning process yourself, it is necessary to go through each sequence in the programme in the greatest possible detail. Time you spend thinking before production starts will mean time saved in making the programme. And in programme-making, time is money.

Costing programmes

If your decision was to hire a producer and you've briefed him or her thoroughly, there's not much for you to do during the making of the programme, except to get what enjoyment you can from watching someone else spending your money. When the production process is complete you'll have what you bought — a programme to form the basis of an interactive video system. The cost will be considerable. Different producers make different charges. But it is not unusual for them to charge £1000 for each minute of programme material. That pays for the planning, scripting, lighting, shooting, editing and all the inter-connected and related bits and pieces. Everything costs money. The writer needs paying; the actors receive fees; copyright holders need paying; music doesn't come free and musicians are expensive; there's a charge for every mile travelled by every vehicle; every meal eaten on location has to be paid for out of the programme budget; the production team will not be prepared to stay in the cheapest available bed-and-breakfast establishment.

The list isn't endless, but it is long. It's impossible to say what the average programme will cost, because there isn't an average programme. Every one is a one-off. But it would be difficult to find a producer prepared to agree to deliver even the simplest 25 minute programme for £2500. Such a cost — £100 a minute — buys you the most rudimentary of talking head sequences. For £25 000 for 25 minutes you should get an all-singing, all-dancing show, should you want one. And if you want it to be all-star as well, £25 000 may not be enough.

The sensible thing to do, once you have sorted out your brief, is to get quotations from a number of producers or production companies. But be sure you are getting quotations and not estimates. A quotation can be the basis of a fixed-price contract. An estimate assumes no fixing of prices; the final cost could be smaller — theoretically — but invariably it's greater. Whatever you do, don't embark on the project without a contract which you consider to be satisfactory. If friends are involved, a contract is even more desirable.

Scripting programmes

One essential document with which you will be involved is the script. After you've briefed the producer, a script will be prepared It's vital that you should be happy with the script. If you're not, there's little chance that you will be happy with the production. Scripts are complicated, but their essential ingredients are simple. A script is the document on which the programme is based. It will contain all the basic ingredients which you have given the producer in your briefings, and it will be a detailed statement of how he or she intends to realize the programme.

It's important that you should check that all the basic ingredients are there and that the emphases on various aspects are satisfactory to you. It's reasonable for you to insist on satisfaction here. In fact, it's sensible to include provision for this in the contract. Further, you're entitles to express opinions on the pictures and sounds proposed, but conceiving and executing them are the producer's business, so it would not be reasonable for you to expect control over them.

There are two basic advantages to hiring professional production expertise. The first is that you don't have to do the hard work yourself. The second is that, if you've hired the right people, you can be reasonably assured of a satisfactory product; it may even be more than satisfactory.

There are disadvantages. There's the cost; but once you've agreed a price, it's profitless worrying about that. The main disadvantage is that once you've hired a dog to bark for you, it's pointless trying to bark yourself. A producer will expect to be allowed to get on with the making of a programme without interference from the person who commissioned it. Some will make gestures towards discussions during the production process, if you ask for them. Some won't even go that far. And some will insist on being left to get on with it.

So, you've handed over control of your project to someone else. If you trust them, there's no problem. Nor will there be, as long as they deserve your trust. If you don't trust your producer you've chosen the wrong person, or you were the wrong person to make the choice. If you found the final script acceptable, the chances are that you won't experience any problems of confidence. The producer will need to deliver a satisfactory product if he or she is to prosper.

Scripts for programme production appear in a variety of forms, but they all have common ingredients. It's usual to have two main columns on each page dividing the page roughly into two halves. On the left is the vision column and on the right is the sound column, sometimes called audio.

The idea is to put details of each shot, one after the other, in the left hand column, and to put information about sound — the words, music, or whatever, in the right-hand column. Each shot is numbered on the left, usually, which gives you an ancillary column. Also, the duration in seconds, or minutes and seconds, appears in another ancillary column to the right, after the audio information. If you're working with more than one camera in a continuous sequence, information about which camera is taking which shot is also contained in the script.

Everything you intend to do during the course of the making of the programme should appear in the script. Everything must be written down. Nothing should be left to memory, or to odd pieces of paper, which may or may not be to hand when they are needed.

Preparing storyboards

Before you start work on the script, you may find it useful to prepare a storyboard. That's a document with pictures (usually hand-drawn by the compiler) on the left, and information on the right. The purpose of the pictures is to give an idea of what the shots are going to look like in the production. The purpose of the information is to amplify the sketches and to give details of the sound which is to accompany the pictures. Any other relevant information can be included as well.

If you're going to make up a storyboard, and it's by no means essential to do so, remember that if the screen is to be filled by your picture, it must be in a horizontal to vertical ratio of four by three. An ability to draw is not a prerequisite for successful production. And if you can't draw, your storyboard will look odd. Many producers see pictures in their mind, and nowhere else, until the time for shooting comes. Then they see them through the viewfinder or on the monitor.

Sample script.

Shot	VISION. Camera Description.	SOUND. Narrative....and information about music and effects. (Duration)
1	Camera 3 Wide shot of table littered with scripts	Scripts for programme production appear in a variety of forms, but they all have common ingredients. (6")
2	Camera 2 Close shot of single script	Everything you intend to do during the course of making the programme should appear in the script. (6")

3	Camera 2 Mid shot of producer writing	Everything must be written down (2")
4	Camera 4 Close shot of pen moving across paper	Nothing should be left to memory. (2")

Figure 1 shows a simple start to a straightforward script. The cameras are used in whatever order is most effective. It's as well to leave plenty of room on your script so that alterations and notes can be written in. Scripts can get exceedingly complicated. And there's not just one kind. There's a shooting script, which is used usually for single-camera shooting. There's a recording script, which is used usually for multi-camera recording. And, apart from any others, there's an editing script, which is used for editing. For most programmes it's possible to combine all the necessary elements into one script. It could well be a long document, but it has to be comprehensive.

When you're preparing a script, remember to include all the information that anyone involved in the production can conceivably need to know. And remember that it's advisable that everybody should know most things, if not everything about the production. It's a team effort and it's not a good idea to lock individual members of the team into compartments. If they're encouraged properly, it's possible that individuals will have more to contribute to the success of the enterprise than a straightforward definition of their functions will demand.

So, you work out the pictures you want to record to make up the sequences in your production. You describe them in the script. You allocate them to cameras, if you're working with more than one. And you decide which words, effects, music will accompany the pictures. In short, you visualize the production shot by shot, and you write it all into the script.

Preparing for shooting

When you've finished the script you'll have a good idea of what the finished programme will look like and how it will sound. But when you've reached that stage, there's still work to be done on the script before shooting starts. The order of shooting or recording must be decided. If, for example you are working on location (which means, usually, more than one location) you may need shots with a particular background at several places in the script. If you started shooting at the beginning of the script and took each shot in order, you could return to the particular background several times.If you did it that way you'd be wasting time and money and energy.

The efficient way to resolve the problem is to compile a shooting order for the shots in your script. While you're doing this compilation, remember the logistics involved in travelling from location to location, and remember also those involved in setting up camera, sound and possibly, lights at different places in the same location.

An alternative is to prepare a separate shooting script, with locations and shots in the order you are going to record them. But that is not necessary except for the most complicated of programmes. A well-contrived programme script and a shooting order is enough for most cases.

Whatever you shoot will need editing. It's sensible to remember this when you are preparing the script and when you are shooting. If you make the right decisions during recording you can prevent all kinds of problems arising during editing. If you are using one camera only, every shot will have to be joined to another one. If you are using more than one camera, and recording in sequences containing a number of shots each, you'll be able to decide whether or not each sequence works when you watch the play-back after each recording. But the sequences will need to be edited together for the final programme.

At this stage, before a camera has turned, or a frame been recorded, it's useful to remember that you are not engaged in the production of a television programme, which will be transmitted once and then, perhaps, repeated once or twice. The sequences of an interactive video programme will be seen time after time by the individuals using it. There's little chance that they won't notice any flaws. In fact, there's every chance that flaws could divert their attention.

Just as it's important to remember that the sequences will be repeated, it's important to visualize how each sequence will look in isolation and what image will be on the screen when the sequence is stopped.

In summary, all thinking should be done during the preparation of the script; and the script must be comprehensive. But it isn't written in stone and flexibility during shooting is entirely desirable. If a good idea comes to you, or to any other member of the team, during shooting, if you're sure that it's better than what was planned, and if you're sure it will fit in the programme properly — the sensible thing to do is to use it.

When you've reached this stage (and probably sooner) you'll realize that as there are so many things to think about and to do it would be a good idea to keep a record of everything. There are a variety of ways to keep records. In some production offices you'll see large blackboards, or whiteboards. containing columns of information. Details are entered of all the tasks that need to be done, by whom and by when. As each task is completed, confirmation appears on the board. It's a combination of check list and record of work done. It's by no means essential to use a blackboard, or even a clipboard, but the important thing is to keep a record in whatever way suits you, just as long as it works — and every member of the team understands it. Nothing must be left to chance or to memory, which is often the same thing. Some small task not completed satisfactorily or to time can have a disastrous effect on a production, and delays are expensive.

Assembling a production team

When you've thought about everything during the preparation of your script, you'll have realized that producing programmes is a team effort. If you're going to produce, you'll need a team to help you. The kind of team will depend on the kind of production.

There's a degree of confusion about what producers do in production. In essence, they are the people with the overall responsibility. Sometimes they hire a director to actually make the programme. You may decide to do so, if you're producing a programme. It will cost you several thousand pounds, depending on the work involved.You may decide to save money and do the direction yourself. That would be cheaper, certainly, but unless you know what you're doing it could be costly in the long run. A badly directed production is unlikely to form the basis of a successful interactive video programme.

Whoever directs, a production secretary will be needed. He or she will be responsible for all the paperwork. If the production is a large scale one you may need ordinary secretaries as well. Production secretaries need to have special skills. It's inefficient to prevent them from exercising these skills by insisting that they take time out to undertake ordinary secretarial tasks.

You'll need an organizer. In simple productions, it's possible for the production secretary to look after the organization, with supervision. But it's vital that the organization runs smoothly.

Somebody will need to perform the functions of stage manager. This could be left to the secretary, as well. But,even in simple production, the secretary can't do everything.

Needs vary so vastly, depending on the nature of the production. The most sensible approach to take is to analyse carefully the various functions that have to be carried out—and make sure there are enough people to undertake them. But, at the same time, make sure there aren't too many people. It's possible that during the course of the production of a programme someone could be hired to perform a task that occurs only rarely. That person could spend 5 per cent of his or her time working and 95 per cent of it waiting around. That's expensive. Try and hire people who are able and willing to turn their hands to a number of different duties.

Preparing for location work.

When you've assembled your basic team, it's time to start your reconnaissance. If you're going to work on location, you may need to visit a number of places before you find locations which will be suitable. While you're looking, remember that the team and its vehicle will need to get to the location and that overnight accommodation may be needed. And remember that you have no control over the weather. If your script calls for a fine day, it will probably rain and vice versa.

You must decide whether or not you need a power supply If you decide to work with batteries, they'll need recharging. People will need to eat and drink, and go to the loo.

So it isn't simply a matter of finding places that fit the script. As in all production work, you'll find that you have to make choices. Some decisions will be easy, others will be difficult.Basically, its a matter of priorities. You may know of an ideal location that involves an extra three days travelling for 30 seconds of programme material. You have to decide whether or not the journey is necessary. And if you think it's necessary, you have to decide if it's affordable.

After the recces are completed, it's time to draw up a schedule. This will cover travel, accommodation and shooting.Remember that you do not necessarily need everybody at every location on every day. For anyone to travel anywhere is going to cost the production money. Make the schedule comprehensive.If necessary, split travel and accommodation from shooting. Make sure everyone gets a copy in plenty of time, and do your best to see that they read it and understand it.

In some productions it's advisable to take a cameraman with you on your recces. It'll be expensive, but it may be worth it. Alternatively, you could take him after the recces to the locations you've decided to use. Whatever your decision, it's wise to have a planning meeting with all the senior members of the team before shooting starts. If it's a small team,hold a planning meeting for everyone. Involvement tends to enhance performances.

After the planning meeting, it may be necessary to issue a document setting out your programme requirements. Again whether or not you do this depends on the nature and the complexity of your programme. Such a document gives details of cameras, lenses and mounts, microphones, video and sound recorders and lights — and anything else of a mainly technical nature. If one is issued, it is likely that most people will turn up with the right equipment.

Your production may not call for any location work, so your schedule will be far simpler and deal only with the logistics of your day or days in the studio. If your production is to be based in a studio, it will need to be planned just as carefully as location-based productions are planned. Every minute spent n a studio costs money.

Hiring a studio

If you're hiring a studio, what you'll get for your money is the studio, its equipment (vision, sound and lights) and the people to operate the equipment. Depending on he studio, the cost ranges from hundreds of pounds per day to thousands of pounds, including meal breaks. You'll be lucky to achieve more than five hours of rehearsal and recording in an eight hour day. And overtime is prohibitively expensive.

Unless you plan to work against the simplest of backgrounds, you'll need a designer to create sets for you. These will have a short life, if a useful one. But you will find them expensive.

You may need a graphics designer as well as a set designer. He or she will look after all the words you intend to display in vision, either with their own backing or superimposed over other pictures. Some studios contain electronic graphic generating machines, with reasonably sophisticated type fonts. Most productions find them more than adequate.

The chances of your being allowed to do your own direction in a studio are not great. They tend to be unionized; and even if they aren't, they're so complicated that you'd probably waste more money by taking so long to do everything than you'd have saved by not hiring an experienced director.

Working on location with a single camera is a different proposition. If you have the necessary ability to organize things reasonably efficiently, and some inkling of what makes a good picture and a good sequence of pictures, you have a chance of succeeding. The chance is increased considerably if you hire a cameraman with the inclination to be helpful. Many cameramen have experience of directing. All of them have experience of working with directors, and a large number think they are able to direct themselves. Their advice can be invaluable. Their cooperation is essential. If the cameraman is not committed to the success of the production, it has little chance of succeeding.

The choice of whether to make your production studio-based or location-based may be a simple one. Some productions call for a great amount of studio work and a small amount of location work. For others, the ratio is reversed. If most of your production is to be in a studio, it may not be economically sensible to go to the expense of location shooting for a small percentage of the total running time. On the other hand, if most of your work is to be done on location, hiring a studio for the odd sequence or two is likely to be prohibitively expensive. Your decision is likely to be a compromise between what's desirable and what's affordable. If you don't have to compromise, you're lucky.

Whatever your decision is, there are more planning processes to undertake before shooting starts. Transport has to be arranged, accommodation may need to be booked. You'll need to make sure that all the stationery of various kinds that you'll need will be where you need it at the times you'll need it. If you're working on location, you'll need to think of the clothes that you'll need. What's comfortable in an air-conditioned office is rarely appropriate in a muddy field.

Choosing film or videotape

Reasonably early in the planning process, you'll need to decide whether your production is to be film based or videotape based. There are various film formats and various tape formats. But whatever your decision is, before it is transferred to videodisc, your production will need to be transferred to 1" C Format videotape. It'll be called the master tape and it will need to conform to a precise specification, of which more later.

That doesn't mean that your programme will have to be originated on 1" C Format videotape. Within reason, you can originate your programme material on the film or videotape format of your choice. But one vital requirement is that the picture and sound quality is of a sufficiently high standard to be acceptable on the final videodisc. Every time a sequence is copied, its quality will be lowered to a greater or lesser extent. So the objective must be to copy as little as possible. Every copy is called a generation, and every time copying is involved the material is subjected to to what is called de-generation.

If you are considering using film for your production, the choices available are between 35mm, 16mm, or smaller. It's as well to forget the smaller formats because the chances of the finished material being of a sufficiently high technical standard are negligible. The smaller formats were created for amateur, home-movie use and they are perfectly adequate for that. But there's little professional equipment available to handle 8mm, or super 8, or whatever; and by the time they've reached a videodisc, the pictures just would not be good enough.

In fact, the 16mm format was developed in America for amateur use. But as the quality of the cameras, lenses and film improved, it became used widely for professional production. To-day, 35mm filming is prohibitively expensive. The stock is expensive in the first place, and all the equipment necessary to use the format is far more expensive than the 16mm equivalent. The quality is better, undoubtedly. But, for a production intended for videodisc, it's difficult to conceive a set of circumstances under which it would be justifiable to go the extra expense.

So, if you are going to make your production on film, you have, realistically, no choice — you'll make it on 16mm The equipment available is sophisticated and light in weight. The film stock available is wide-ranging.

Before dealing with the advantages and disadvantages of using film, it's sensible to look, briefly, at the videotape formats available. These are expressed in inches, rather than millimetres, because the French were not so involved in pioneering them. The first successful videotape system was developed in America.

The task facing the developers was to devise a system for recording the electronic signals which make up a television picture, and for replaying them. When television started, in the 1930s, all picture were live — there was no means of recording them. It was possible to transmit images recorded on film, optical images, by, basically, pointing a television camera at the film, or a projection of the film. Film on television is treated similarly to-day, although the systems used for doing this are much advanced from the early systems in reliability, fidelity, flexibility and sophistication. Losses in quality are not discernible.

The first successful videotape recording system used tape that was two inches wide. There were four recording heads on a revolving drum. The machines were large and expensive. Early forms of editing involved cutting the tape and rejoining it. The machines became smaller over the years, but hardly less expensive, and methods were developed for editing by transferring images and sounds from one machine to another. In the most sophisticated editing applications, several machines were used and the editing was controlled by computer.

It was a cumbersome system and having to use four heads was a disadvantage, but it worked and the quality was excellent. Because it used four heads, it became known as quadruplex.But because it used four heads, it could only achieve a straightforward replay of a recording. It was not capable of slow-motion replays or freeze frames. The reason for this was that if the tape was slowed or stopped, the four heads could not function satisfactorily. Another problem was that it was not possible to check the recording while it was being made. You saw, on a monitor, what was going into the machine. But you had to wait until the recording finished before you could replay and check whether or not the material was satisfactorily recorded. And then, to be safe, you had to check the whole of the recording. If you simply spot-checked, all you could be sure of was that the spots you checked were satisfactory.

The next development in video followed a reverse procedure to what happens normally — it was developed for amateur use and then refined for professional use. It uses two heads on a revolving drum and is called helical scan, because the tape forms a helix shape when it is loaded around the drum. Apart from the number of heads, there is an important fundamental difference between helical scan and quad. In the helical scan system, every rotation of the drum achieves a complete recording of a single frame.

This has a number of advantages: the tape doesn't have to be so wide, so the equipment doesn't have to be so cumbersome; it is possible to vary the speed of replay; it is possible to replay a single frame; and it is possible to check what's recorded on the tape as the recording proceeds.

If you have a video machine at home, it will use the helical scan system. Even the earliest machines used it. But in the early years the system did not work well enough for professional use — it took some time for a satisfactory professional system to be developed. But when it was, the quad system lost its monopoly of the professional market. The professional standard became 1" helical scan. It began with A-format and developed through B-format to C-format — the one required for a master tape from which videodiscs are to be manufactured.

The system you use at home will probably be VHS, which stands for Video Home System, or it may be Betamax. Both use half-inch tapes, and both suffer from similar disadvantages to those present in the smaller film formats — the quality is not good enough for the use to which the finished programme will be put.

There's another helical scan system which uses half inch tapes and does meet professional specifications. It's used widely by television news-gathering operations throughout the world. Basically, it's a scaled down alternative to the professional 1" system. It has advantages because the equipment necessary is smaller and, therefore, the recorder can be attached to the camera chassis.This makes for far more flexible news coverage.

The professional half-inch system has replaced a three-quarter-inch system as the favourite electronic system for television news gathering. The three-quarter-inch system was too heavy-weight to oust 16mm film entirely. But it is still used for closed circuit systems and various industrial and institutional purposes. It comes in two forms — high-band and low-band. The high-band variant is superior to the low-band one. The difference in cost is not great, and it's advisable to consider only high-band for your programme.

Other systems use narrower tape, and they are beginning to achieve surprisingly high standards of recording and reproduction.

So, there's a wide choice of tape formats available. Given the disadvantages of the 2" format, it's as well to exclude it — unless your production is to be studio based and the studio you're going to use comes equipped only with 2" recording.

That leaves the choice between high-band three-quarter-inch, professional half-inch and the new smaller tape formats. Three-quarter inch could well be cheaper than half-inch, but half-inch provides a better picture quality and the equipment is less bulky.

Improving sound quality

One of the problems with all film and videotape systems is that if the sound is recorded on the side of the film or on a track on the videotape, it is not of a particularly high quality. For speech only this may not be a problem. But if you intend to film or videorecord music, it does become a problem. In film cameras, in order to capture a sharp image, the film stops for a fraction of a second. In fact, during one second, 24 separate pictures are taken. On the types of film stock used for recording sound, there's a thin strip of magnetic tape near the edge of the film; it's on this strip that the sound is recorded. But sound cannot be recorded on to stationary tape or, satisfactorily, on to tape which pauses 24 times a second. So the film is laced in the camera with a loop between the picture gate and the sound recording head. This allows the film to start and stop at the picture gate and to move without pause past the sound recording head. That works well enough for speech, but it's not ideal for music.

On videotape there's a different problem. So much of the space on the tape is taken up with recording the vision and various necessary control tracks that there's not a great amount left for recording the sound. Still, some videotape systems offer the facility of recording two separate tracks of sound. And, generally, the quality of the sound on videotape is better than that on film. Again, both are adequate for speech, but struggle with music.

There's a simple way to improve the quality of the sound you record. You link a high quality sound recorder to your camera, whether it's a film camera or an electronic one. But you must make sure that the camera and the recorder run synchronously (in synch). There are various ways of doing this. Which way you do it doesn't matter, as long as the result is right. Most film cameras are able to accept sound synchronizing systems easily. It's not always as easy with electronic cameras. Some, like the up-to-the-minute camcorders with built-in recorder, are designed for compactness and portability. Both of these attributes would be dissipated if separate recorders were linked to them. But if you want high quality sound,there s no alternative readily available.

Choosing cameras

Which film camera you use is largely a matter of personal preference.Every camera operator will have a favourite. The important thing to remember is to use a good one. Given a skilled operator, the quality of the pictures depends to a large extent on the quality of the camera.

Which electronic camera you use is a more complicated question. If you hire a studio, you'll use the cameras with which it is equipped. They'll be on the heavy side and not particularly portable. Similar cameras will be used on what are called outside broadcasts. These are multi-camera productions where most, if not all, of the facilities available in a studio are available in a mobile form. So far, most of these cameras will have three tubes in order to achieve colour pictures. Various means of producing colour pictures from one tube have been devised, but none of them are accepted generally as achieving professional standards.

In a three-tube camera, one tube looks after the blues, another the greens and a third the reds. Because three tubes are involved, it's important that the cameras are lined up and the tubes registered with great precision. In the early days of colour television the cameras were large and weighed as much as 200 pounds They're considerably smaller and lighter now, and they're considerably more reliable than they used to be.

As well as conventional cameras, there's a whole new generation of light-weight cameras available now. These were developed specifically for use in circumstances where, hitherto, light-weight film cameras were the only option. Many use three tubes still, but the tubes are smaller than in conventional cameras.

Then, there's a new type of camera which does not use any tubes at all. These are solid state cameras in which electronic chips perform the functions which in conventional cameras are performed by the tubes. They constitute a major technological breakthrough. They're exceedingly light and portable and they're extremely reliable. Modern tubed cameras are capable of lining themselves up automatically. Some come even with built-in or add-on computer-based fault diagnosing and correcting systems.

Solid state cameras have less to go wrong and come equipped with even more automatic goodies.

Another major achievement is associated with solid state cameras. Most technical developments in television led to greater sophistication and flexibility in production techniques. Inevitably, the programmes became more complicated. But, not only was more and more equipment needed to produce the programmes, each piece of equipment was more expensive than whatever it was it was replacing.

Solid state cameras seem to be breaking new ground as far as costs go. They're not only better; they're cheaper! For little more than £1000 you can buy cameras with built-in video recorders which provide crackingly sharp pictures and entirely reasonable sound. The tape formats they use are the small ones — quarter-inch and similar — and that's a disadvantage as far as interactive video programmes are concerned. It's doubtful that they have reached yet the stage where it is possible to transfer the sound and vision signals to a professional system for editing without unacceptable degradation.

Rehearsing the Arguments

The arguments about whether or not film is superior to video are still raging. Film used to have advantages in portability. But video matches it in this respect, even if it has not overtaken it.

There are those who argue that film is a medium which is capable of being used for greater artistry. These proponents claim that the intrinsic quality of pictures on film surpasses that of pictures on video. They consider video pictures to be too sharp and lifelike and altogether lacking in atmosphere.

Others argue that the degree of artistry or atmosphere you get from either film or video is related directly to the amount of whichever commodity you put into it. Proponents of video claim that it is more flexible than film.

If you're sensible, you'll make your decision on which medium to use after careful consideration of what you require in your programme, and of which medium is the more likely to meet your requirements with the greater degree of satisfaction. It's worth remembering that the editing processes, of which more later. And it's worth remembering that you can replay a video recording as soon as you want to after you have made it. This enables you to check not only that you have something in the can, but exactly what it is you do have in the can, Such a facility is well worth having and if used properly can lead to easier and more effective editing.

Choosing lenses

Whether you decide to work with film or with video it's important to consider also what lenses you will use. A similar range is available for use in both mediums. Zoom lenses are available universally and their range is large. There are many advantages to a zoom lens with a wide range; perhaps the simplest is that you can frame exactly the shot you want without having to move the camera much, if at all. A disadvantage is that they require more light than ordinary lenses. But modern cameras are extremely sensitive — so zooms are used universally now. Separate lenses are used rarely, except when special effects are necessary, and most of these can be achieved with zoom lenses and special adaptors.

Starting shooting

So, you've gone through all the processes necessary for the preparation of your programme. The team is assembled; the script is ready; the equipment has been checked; all the logistical arrangements have been made. It's time to start shooting.

PROGRAMME MAKING

You'll remember that the shooting order does not necessarily follow the programme order. Getting your first shot right is important. Getting every shot right is important. But the first one is particularly so. The way you achieve it is likely to set the pattern for the shooting of the whole production. You've visualized what you want. Now's the time to rehearse it. It's not only dramas or entertainments that need rehearsal. The simplest of factual programmes need rehearsal. If you're working with electronics, as opposed to film, it's entirely possible to roll the cameras on the first run-through — and to keep them rolling until you're satisfied with the sequence. But it's not a good idea to mount your production this way. Members of the team may well find it frustrating, or confusing, or both. The chances of getting the sequence right in the first two or three takes without rehearsal are negligible. Some members of the team will have done their jobs satisfactorily from the start. Others won't. That's entirely reasonable, some tasks are more complicated than others. The most sensible thing to do is to run through a sequence until every member of the team knows what's wanted from the sequence and what's required from them in the sequence. Then rehearse the sequence until everybody is happy and until you are confident that you're going to get what you want.

During this process, if you establish a reasonable working relationship with your team, you could well find that individuals will make suggestions as to how your ideas may be realized. There's always the chance that somebody else's suggestion may be an improvement on what you've decided to do. If it is, accept it. There's absolutely no point in doing it your way — and getting it wrong. It's equally pointless letting your pride prevent you from improving your production.

You rehearse until everyone is ready. It's important to make sure that the sound is right, as well as the vision. It's too easy to concentrate on the vision and to forget about the sound. But sometimes achieving good quality sound is extremely difficult. You don't want booms and microphones spoiling your shots. But you do need good sound. Modern equipment is extremely flexible. It's surprising what can be achieved by skillful operators with gun mics and rifle mics, and the like. And it's not necessary to have wires everywhere. Radio mics are extremely reliable. And, as their name implies, they operate without wires. But they do need careful setting up.

If you're working in a studio, lights form part of the basic equipment. If you're working on location, you may be able to manage with available light, given the right filters for your lenses. Just as with sound equipment, modern cameras are extremely flexible, but they do need minimum light levels, and if these levels are not available, your production will have to provide them. Most camera teams carry some lights with them, enough for simple set-ups involving small areas and few people. But if you want to light a crowded cathedral, or something similar, it's going to be expensive.

When you've finished rehearsing, you go for a take. If you're working on film, the chances are you won't have been tempted to start shooting without adequate rehearsal. Film stock is too expensive to be wasted by taking unnecessary chances. Having gone for the first take, you go on shooting until you are sure you have achieved a satisfactory take. How many takes you shoot on each sequence is up to you. There's no point in finishing your day's shooting ahead of schedule and ending up with a set of sequences that are less satisfactory than they would have been if you'd taken more time and trouble. But there's also no point in finishing your day so far behind schedule that you have no chance of ever catching up. You're in charge, so it's up to you to get it right.

If you're working with film, you'll have seen with your own eyes and heard with your own ears what happened during the take, or takes. But you won't see what's on the exposed film until it's been processed and a print prepared for viewing. It follows that you have to rely on your cameraman or woman. There's nothing wrong with that. Producers and directors have done so since the earliest days of the cinema. But, even if whoever is operating the camera is entirely reliable, you'll never be certain that a sequence is what you want until you have seen it on film. That's why rushes came into being. The word is used because it describes what happens to the film after it's been exposed. It's rushed to the laboratories for processing and print making, and then rushed to the producer or director, or both, for viewing. If you're working on location this presents problems. You'll need to view the film before you can be sure you've finished your location work. So you'll have to make arrangements for viewing facilities to be available. Or you'll have to travel to somewhere where viewing facilities are available.

If you're working with electronics, it's a simple matter to have each take replayed as soon as is convenient after it's been shot. You can see actually what you've got as soon as you've got it, and you can be sure whether or not it's satisfactory. Given that your production is intended for an interactive video programme, its particularly important that you know precise details of every shot and every sound. When the programme is used, some sequences may be seen time and time again. Every frame in every sequence must be be as right as you can get it. Being able to see a sequence immediately it's been recorded should enable you to be certain it's satisfactory there and then. And that should lead to a satisfying sense of security.

If your programme is to include existing material, it's sensible to have those sequences copied onto the format of video tape which you are using for shooting, whether you are working in a studio, or on location, or both. Then you will be able to check how the existing material will slot into the material you are shooting. As part of your preparation you will have planned, of course, how it will all fit together. But there's only one satisfactory way of making sure, and that's to see each sequence and each shot and to check everything carefully.

Inserting time code

Another sensible thing to do, if you're working on videotape, is to see that what's called time code is inserted on all the material you originate. That means that electronic signals giving the time elapsed in minutes, seconds and hundredths of seconds will be inserted into the pictures you shoot. It's usual to start at zero on the first frame of the first shot and to start the electronic clock running whenever you shoot. If the first shot lasts for seven seconds and 55 hundredths of a second, the digital time display will start at 00 minutes 00 seconds and 00 hundredths and finish at 00 minutes 07 seconds and 55 hundredths. The information will be displayed in a manner similar to that used on television transmissions of some sporting events, like races at athletics meetings, or downhill skiing and the like. To continue the example, if the second shot lasts for nine seconds and five hundredths of a second, the digital display will start at 00 minutes 07 seconds and 56 hundredths and finish at 00 minutes 16 seconds and 60 hundredths. The total will accumulate as the shooting progresses.

The idea is to have these electronic signals available when you want them during the process of planning your editing and during the editing itself. They are capable of being switched into and out of the picture at will. If you were worrying that you might end up with a programme with digital time displays in your pictures, you can relax. That won't happen, but you will find time code displays an extremely useful aid.

If you're working with more than one camera, in a studio or on location, you'll probably end up with sequences containing a number of shots rather than a series of individual shots. Using more than one sequence is usually wasteful. The production secretary will keep a record of the start and finish time codes for each sequence. This will be done, probably, on a copy of the script. It doesn't matter if it's the shooting script or the programme script. If you're working with both at the same time, a record should be kept on a stopwatch, just in case there's a problem with the time code.

If you're working with a single camera, the production secretary will keep what's called a shot list. This will be a record of the individual shots in the order that they are taken. If you're working on videotape with time code, that will be incorporated in the shot list and checked against stopwatch timings. If you're working with film, the production secretary will include in the shot list information about which shots are on which roll of film. With videotape, the shot list contains information about cassettes or spools.

Leaving nothing to chance

By keeping to these procedures you'll be doing as much as possible to check that everything you planned to shoot for your production is in fact shot. Nothing should be left to chance, or to memory. But while you're shooting you'll also be looking forward to editing. Comprehensive notes on a script and a carefully compiled shot list will be invaluable. And, again on the principle that it's better to leave nothing to chance or to memory, make sure that the script, or the shot list, or both, contain notes of the editing possibilities of which you've thought during shooting.

On videotape it's possible to shorten the editing time required for your programme by using a procedure that's called assemble editing. This involves programming the video recorder to run to the end of one shot and to start recording at the beginning of the next shot. It's necessary to review the first shot and to decide precisely when it is to finish. Then the out point is cued on the recorder. The next step is to rehearse the next shot until everyone is ready to take it and then to line it up on the camera. The recorder then runs on a cue for, say, ten seconds; the seconds are counted down and the action starts for the next shot. If it sounds complicated, it's because it is. It fact, it's a relatively simple technique to use technically, but the complications arise from trying to get the timing of the edit absolutely right from a production point of view. The chances of success are not great. You could well end up wasting more time in shooting than you are likely to save in editing. And the result may not be satisfactory, anyway. If it isn't, you'll have to try and improve the edit during an editing session, but it may not be possible to achieve improvement because you shot the material for an assemble edit and it's not appropriate for a post-shooting edit.

You're not likely to be using the VHS format for shooting, because it's too cheap and cheerful and the quality is not good enough. But cheap and cheerful are useful qualities in themselves and it's as well to take advantage of them. When you get to editing on professional equipment, you'll find the hire charges are high. The equipment is expensive to buy and maintain and a great deal of skill and experience and skill is demanded to use it effectively. So, it's sensible to use the cheapest available satisfactory equipment while you're planning your edits. This is where VHS comes in. The quality is good enough for you to see and hear what you've got on the professional tapes. So, have a VHS copy made of all your programme material. This can be done during shooting, if it's convenient; if it isn't, have it done after shooting has been completed. Make sure that the copy contains time code.

It's sensible to think about editing while you're shooting. But it's important to remember your priority. That is to be sure that you shoot all the material you require for your programme and that you shoot it as effectively and as imaginatively as possible. And you must always remember the use to which your programme is going to be put. It isn't something which will be seen once, or, possibly, twice. The chances are that each sequence will be seen time and time again. And it's entirely possible that the order in which the sequences will be seen may vary.

Getting Organized

Getting your production well organized is largely a matter of understanding the practicalities involved and setting about achieving them. Imagination is something else. Whatever it is, it isn't something you acquire by reading a trainer's guide, or by reading anything else. You've either got or you haven't got style. The same is true of imagination.

How long it takes to shoot a production depends on a number of factors. One is the complexity of the production, another is the type of facilities used on the production, a third factor is the degree of efficiency with which the aims of the production are realized.

If you're working in an electronic studio with four cameras or more, it's unlikely that your production should take more than a day to record; it's unlikely that it will take less than a day. But the costs involved run into thousands of pounds, depending on the facilities. So the chances of you being able to afford more than a day or two at the most, are remote. At the other extreme, if you're shooting on film at a large number of locations, the chances are that you'll be shooting for a week, if not more. The costs involved in hiring a single film crew are much lower than those involved in hiring a multi-camera studio. But film stock is more expensive than video tape. As a rough guide, one day in the studio should cost about the same as a week or ten days shooting on film on location.   Electronic camera crews are dearer to hire than film crews, because the equipment is more expensive. But you should be able to shoot a similar amount of programme material in less time, so the equation is likely to balance here as well.

If you're aiming at a running time for your finished programme of 30 minutes or so, it's sensible to plan to record sufficient material during one day in a studio — perhaps a long day, or a minimum of three days and a maximum of five days on location. If you take longer, it will cost more; if you take less time, it will cost less money.

Editing Film

When you've finished shooting, you reach the stage where you review your material and start planning your editing. As always, efficient planning is essential.

Whether you're working on film or on videotape, the end product will be a completed programme. But the editing processes are different. Take film first. Your material will have been shot on negative stock. So a print will be made for you to review and edit. There's no need for this print to be colour-graded, as the show print will be; all you need is an editing print which will be reasonably rough and ready. While the print is being processed, the quarter-inch tapes on which the sound was recorded will be dubbed to magnetic stock of the same gauge as the film you used - 16 millimetre, no doubt. If the editing machine you are using is capable of handling them, you may decide to use two sound tracks. In which case, when you start editing, the machine will be loaded with three spools; one will contain the print of the pictures and the other two the sound dubbed on to magnetic stock. The editor will ensure that the sound track, or tracks, are in synch with the pictures. That's the purpose of the clapperboard that was shot at the beginning of every take. Then you start editing.

You will have planned your edits from the shooting script and the shot list before you start in the editing room. The equipment is not as expensive as electronic equipment, but it's still expensive and there's no point in paying for it before you need it. What you won't be able to plan is which frame ends a shot and which frame starts the next shot. You make that decision with the help of your editor. He or she will operate the machine and will offer you advice as to where to make your edit precisely, in both picture and sound. The editor will have considerable experience and the advice will be well worth heeding. When you've made your decision, the film and sound stock will be cut. The joins will be made either with cement or transparent sticky tape.

A similar procedure is followed for every edit in your programme. If the programme is to run for 30 minutes, there could well be several hundred of them. From your preparation, you'll have an idea of the sequences that will make up your finished programme. But it won't be possible for you to decide each sequence to the last second. So, it's as well to start with a rough cut, which runs slightly longer than is necessary. How much longer, and how rough the cut, depends on you. When the rough cut is finished, you'll have a good idea of the final shape of your programme. Then you and the editor prepare the final cut.

Creating opticals

At this stage, your pictures are assembled in their final order. But work on them has not finished. Because you are working in film, you'll need to plan your optical effects. These range from simple titles and captions over the pictures, or in place of them, to where pictures dissolve into other pictures, or several images are superimposed one over, or after, the other. It's imagination time, again. To achieve this, the editor will assemble two or more reels of film and paper them up with instructions to the processor.

To create an optical effect on film, one set of images is superimposed over another set. Inevitably, this leads to a degree of deterioration; often the final print will be less sharp during the sequences involved; it'll appear grainy. So, it's wise to use opticals only when they're necessary and not as inessential embellishments.

Mixing Sound

Before your final print is prepared, you'll need to complete the work on the sound for your programme. So far, you'll have achieved a series of sequences in sound which match the picture sequences. But the machine on which you've edited the film is not capable of achieving a final sound mix. Just as the film will need optical sound effects, however simple, so will your programme need sound effects. Again, these can be simple mixes from one sound source to another, or they can be complicated sequences with superimpositions and fades and cross fades. All this is the work of the dubbing mixer, and it's done in a dubbing suite. Here you'll find a film projector and an array of equipment. The film editor will prepare as many sound tracks as are necessary to achieve the desired effects and a dubbing chart for the dubbing mixer to follow. You, the film editor, and the dubbing mixer will then rehearse the dub. It's important to get this part of your production right. Sound is not just an incidental. No matter how good the pictures, your production will not succeed unless the sound matches them in quality. Indeed, good sound enhances good pictures.

When you've finished rehearsing the dub, you go for a take. There was a time when you had to get it right in one complete take. If a mistake was made, it was necessary to start again at the beginning and go right through to the end — without a mistake. But flexibility arrived some years ago. Rock and roll dubbing suites, as they're called, enable you to go back to a convenient point before a mistake and restart from there. The film and all the sound tracks stay in synch while you go backwards and forwards — hence rock and roll. So it's not necessary to go back to the beginning after a mistake. You can take as many takes as you decide are necessary. But remember that dubbing suites cost money, as well as every other facility. So don't waste time.

Depending, again, on the complexity of your production, you should be able to dub a 30 minute programme in four hours.

Preparing show prints

When the sound mix is complete, the negative cutter can start work. This involves cutting the negative to match the final cut of the editing print, frame for frame. Each frame has a number near the edge of the film stock, outside the exposed part of the film. The negative cutter works from the numbers. It's a specialized job, and it's not one you or the film editor need to supervize.

When the negative has been cut, it goes to the processor for the preparation of a colour-graded show print, complete with all the opticals. When this is ready, you and the editor check it to see that it is satisfactory. It's wise to check it on a projector rather than an editing machine. You'll be making decisions on the quality of the pictures and the balance of the colours. You can't expect better quality from the print than went into the negative. But you can expect matching quality. The printing process doesn't involve the sound track, so that'll stay as good as it was when it left the dubbing suite. If you accept the show print, then your production is ready for the next stage in the process of preparing an interactive video programme.

Editing Videotape

Before you start editing programme material shot on video tape, you have to take decisions on a number of options which are open to you. The imperative is not to degrade the technical quality of your material. If you've used three-quarter inch tape for origination, there's a limit to the number of generations that are possible without technical deterioration. To be blunt, it'll stand one and no more. If you've used one-inch tape for origination, you shouldn't have a problem; it is, after all, an expensive system. There should be no problems with half-inch tape either. You get that for which you pay.

The problem is concerned with the way in which video tape is edited. In the early days of two-inch tape, the original format, editing was a matter of cutting the tape at the end of a shot or sequence, and rejoining it at the start of the next shot or sequence. It was a rudimentary and time-consuming process, requiring the use of a microscope, a sharp blade, fidgety sticky tape and much manual dexterity. Mixes and dissolves and superimpositions were not possible.

Modern video tape editing techniques are much more sophisticated. The days of physically cutting tape have long since gone. Practically any visual effect is possible. The basis of modern tape editing systems is to transfer shots, or sequences, from one take to another. The simplest of systems require two machines. One is used to select and then replay shots, the other is used to record material for the edited programme. The two machines are linked by an electronic editing device which is programmable for various functions. Theoretically there's no limit to the number of machines that may be linked together for editing. But three should be ample for your programme. The advantage of three-machine editing over two is that you can set up shots on two of the machines and record their output onto the third. In this way you can build up sequences containing mixes, dissolves and superimpositions, and the like.

Given the ability to transfer pictures and sound from one machine to another to another, there's the danger that having transferred a shot, or a sequence, once, and having achieved second-generation pictures, you'll make another transfer and end up with third generation pictures. Every time you go down a generation, there's some deterioration in quality. As long as you don't exceed four or five, the quality remains acceptable on one-inch tape; similarly, there's no problem with half-inch tape, but there is a problem with three-quarter-inch tape. So you may think it's not a good idea to start with three-quarter-inch tape in the first place. And you could be right. But it may be the most economical system available for you to hire, and you may not have a sufficiently large budget to afford anything more expensive. So, if you're going to edit on three-quarter-inch tape, it's imperative that you do not go beyond two generations. If you find this restriction acceptable, then the problem has disappeared. If you don't there is a solution, but it is expensive. If you transfer all your original, first-generation three-quarter-inch material to one-inch, or half-inch, you should acquire a complete set of un-edited programme material, of good technical quality, on the new format. It won't be as good as it would have been if you'd originated the material in the new format, but it will be good enough.

It's not good practice to originate on one format and then transfer to another, but it has to be done sometimes for operational reasons, or as an economy measure. The extra expense occurs because one-inch, and half-inch, editing suites are more expensive to hire than three-quarter-inch suites.

Whatever format you've selected for editing, it's important to spend as little time as possible in an editing suite. Three-machine 1" editing can cost over £1000 a day, so the fewer days you occupy an editing suite, the less money you spend. You'll find there are hourly rates available, but there's usually a requirement for a minimum booking of half-a day. That'll be frustrating,if you need only an hour or two on a second or third day, just to finish your programme. Still, you may be able to negotiate a satisfactory arrangement.

Reviewing, preparing — and starting

So, there are compelling reasons to arrive for the editing session as well prepared as possible. To help achieve this, you use your VHS machine, in the office, at home, or wherever is convenient. You've arranged for VHS tapes of all your programme material to be available to you, complete with time code. The first stage in your preparation is to review all the material you have originated;while you're doing that, refer to your editing notes. Having completed your review, and having read all your editing notes, you are able now to start your editing.If necessary, you can start preparing an editing script.

The most efficient way to edit is not necessarily to start at the beginning of your programme and work your way through to the end. You will not necessarily have shot sequences in the order that they will appear in the final programme. So there's something to be said for planning the editing of the sequences in the order of shooting rather than the order of final assembly. On the other hand, different sequences will be on different spools, or different cassettes, so you may find it preferable to start at the beginning of the programme and work your way through. The VHS cassettes may hold more programme material than the tapes on which it was originated, so you'll be involved in an amount of forward and backward spooling. The time code display will help considerably towards getting this done efficiently. Your notes will give you the start time of each take, so you run forward or backward until you reach the right point. If your VHS has a visual search facility, so much the better.

What you are doing is planning the edits, not executing them. You'll decide which take you are going to use and you'll select the in point and the out point. You'll need to keep a careful record of the decisions and include all the relevant time code information. The process is repeated until the sequence on which you are working is completed. Then you tackle the next sequence and then the subsequent sequences, until you have planned all the edits in your programme.

When you've done all this, you'll have a reasonable idea of how your edited programme will look. It'll be an approximation, because the shots won't be joined together; they'll still be where they were on the tapes before you started he planning of the editing. You won't know how effective the edits you've planned will be. But you will be absolutely familiar with all your material, you will have thought carefully about all your edits and you will have saved much time in an editing suite, and, as always, time is money.

Now you're as ready as you're ever likely to be to start the editing process proper. You arrive for the start of the first editing session with copies of your notes for the editor. He, or she, loads the appropriate tapes on the machines and finds the point at which you plan to begin the first sequence. If you've recorded sound separately, this will be played, in synch, on a separate quarter-inch tape machine or machines, depending on the number of tracks recorded or the number of tracks the editor has decided to use. You decide on the precise point at which the sequence is to start and then the precise point at which it, or the shot, is to end. This information is programmed into the editing device. Then he material is ready for transfer to the programme tape. If you're using three machines for editing, the next shot, or sequence, can be prepared on another machine and that information programmed into the editing device. Then the record machine and the replay machine, or machines, are cued up, ready to run. When they are run, you check that the edit, or edits are satisfactory. And when you are satisfied, the sequence is assembled on the machine loaded with the programme tape. Even if the sound has been recorded on a track, or tracks, on the video tape, it may be necessary to edit it separately. And your editor may decide to prepare separate sound tracks and go through a dubbing process similar to that described for film editing.

During the editing process, you may well find that none of the final edits coincide precisely with those you planned on your VHS machine. You may end up with radically di ferent sequences, or even different sequences in different orders. But the planning yc u put in will have been worthwhile, nevertheless. You'll have saved a great amount of both time and money.

Given the array of sophisticated equipment at your disposal in a three-machine editing suite, it should not take as long to edit a programme shot electronically as it would take to edit a similar programme shot on film. And when the editing is complete, you will have a copy of your programme in its final state. You won't have to wait for neg cutting and the preparation of a graded show print. All your original material will still be on the tapes on which you recorded it. But the programme tape will be the only one which contains your edited programme. This may leave you with a feeling of insecurity. The remedy is to have a copy made in case anything goes amiss with the original. Even if you are not prone to feelings of insecurity, it's wise to have a copy made anyway — if your budget runs to it.

Transferring to videodisc

Whether you used film or videotape to originate your programme, you have reached now the stage where you're ready to start the process of transferring the completed tape to video disc. If you used film, the show print will have to be copied to video tape. The format of the tape must be that which is appropriate for the transfer to video disc.In the United Kingdom the standard used for the video disc is the same as that used for television transmissions — PAL 625 lines/50 fields. The tape system must be one-inch type 'C' Helical. The tapes are called programme master tapes and you need one tape for each disc side that you will be using.

If you originated your programmes on tape, your edited programme may be already on the right format. If it is, it's just a matter of checking that the technical requirements are complied with accurately.If your programme isn't on the right format, you'll need to have it transferred.

The technical specifications for programme master tapes are available from companies who undertake disc pressing.The important thing to remember is that your programme will be reproduced frame by frame on the video disc. So all the shots on the tape must be accurate to a frame, and all the edits must be equally accurate. Whatever artistic content you achieved in your programme remains untouched.

The specialists who undertake the transfer to video disc will provide you with a form to fill in. This must be done carefully. Details of the form and the information required are available from the companies which undertake disc pressing. Your video tape editor, or operator if you're having your programme transferred to a master tape, will help you with the technical details.

There are valid reasons for all the technical requirements, so they must all be met. If you run into problems, consult the specialists before you book the transfer. If necessary, they'll advise you on where to have your master tape made to the necessary specifications.

When it's all over and your videodisc is in use, you may not feel quite like the director of a Hollywood movie who's been nominated for an Oscar. But you may agree that although programme-making is hard work, it's better than having to work for a living.

Chapter 4

COURSEWARE DESIGN

WHAT WILL THE TECHNOLOGY DO?

In the initial preparatory and design stages of an interactive video project, inexperienced designers commonly ask the question: 'What will it do?' Computing specialists frequently reply that the design team or client should assume that 'it will do anything'.

In fact, the question is ill-conceived and the answer is unhelpful. The first task of any project team should be to find which questions to ask.

Those new to interactive video ask the question because they need to know what tools are available, otherwise it is very difficult to visualize the possibilities of course design.

Computing specialists answer that the technology will do anything because they do not wish the designer to feel restricted by technological constraints. This could result in some very poor software.

This very common communication failure between the key members of the project team, however, is likely to result in frustration and tension on both sides. The designer finds it difficult or impossible to visualize the lesson without knowing the possibilities and constraints, and the computing specialist quickly becomes impatient when a workable specification is not delivered.

For example, a trainer designing a slide or worksheet starts with a knowledge of the available tools:-drawing board, ruler, pencils, pens, adhesive, scissors, illustrations, lettering and typescript, photocopying, reduction and other reprographic facilities. The experienced trainer brings this intimate and confident knowledge of available tools and what is or is not possible to the implementation of a particular instructional objective.

In the same way, the interactive video instructional designer must have a clear and confident knowledge of what can be done when considering the layout, content and design of an educational or training programme. There is no reason why this knowledge should be any more harmful to creativity than the artist's intimate knowledge of tools, techniques and colours. Of course, as the designer and the team acquire more experience of working in interactive video they will need to keep abreast of the technological enhancements which become available so that their thinking does not stagnate. It is important not to be tied to one specific approach. Initially, however, you must know what tools are available and what the constraints and the possible problems are. This is not restrictive; it is realistic.

AUDIO VISUAL TOOLS

Moving Video

The first of these tools is the high quality pictorial images obtainable from active-play videodiscs. More detailed information is available in this book about different types of videodisc (see pp 38-42): it is enough to say here that the most commonly used format for IV applications is the CAV laser disc. CLV discs, which were commonly used for feature films and entertainment for the domestic market, are not normally suitable for IV use.

CAV discs are commercially available. Some commercial suppliers of videodiscs seem uncertain themselves whether discs in their catalogues are active-play discs or CLV discs, but it is possible to obtain some usable material. This can be used, if for no other purpose, for experimental work and for testing and practice in the early stages of programme design. It is just possible, although highly unlikely, that you may find video material suitable for your educational and training needs available on an off-the-shelf disc. The use of such discs and the possible complications attaching to such material will be further discussed later.

It is much more likely, however, that you will be working with a videodisc which has been made specifically for your project. Designing the actual content and layout of the video material for your application obviously gives you much more control and caters much more precisely to your needs.

If the whole of a CAV laser disc is taken up with moving video sequences, 30 - 36 minutes of video are available on one side.

Playing modes possible with most industrial videodisc players are normal forward and reverse speeds, fast forward and reverse, scan forward and reverse, step forward or back one frame at a time, and stop. It is also possible to switch audio tracks on and off independently or both together.

Each second of moving video footage on a PAL/SECAM disc is made up of 25 frames, and each frame can be identified by its own individual code number which it receives during the process of mastering. It is possible for the computer program to communicate with the disc player in order to control play from any point to any other point on the disc, or to invoke any of the other playing modes.

Video Stills

Perfect quality still frames can be displayed for indefinite periods without degradation of the picture or damage to the disc. These stills can either be freeze frames taken from a moving video sequence or dedicated slides intended for use as stills only.

If the disc is completely filled with separate still images, up to 54 000 can be held on one side of a disc. This option is usually employed for pictorial databases and high density data storage, although there is no reason why these high quality stills should not play an important part in training or educational applications. However, you could not reproduce 54 000 pages of a book on one side of a laser disc: it will typically require three or four video frames to show a page of A4 printed text legibly on a display screen.

It is also possible to use freeze frames taken from moving sequences as stills in a pictorial database. Generally, however, their value is greatest when they demonstrate a frozen moment of action or interaction - a physical stance, a facial expression illustrating an attitude or a decision, the critical point of a complicated movement, even the hidden thought behind the overt communicative act.

It is, possible to mix moving video footage and dedicated still frames on one disc.

Videodisc Access

Video sequences on tape are read by passing the tape over the read head of the video recorder. The only access possible is linear access, so the tape must be wound physically to the point at which the desired sequence is stored. Although industrial U-matic tape players have very fast rewind times and shorter tapes than those in normal domestic use, tape-based configurations are still unsuited to any IV application which demands very prompt responses from the system. Also, tape-based systems are not suitable for applications which need to access segments of video very precisely. Finally, tape cannot approach the stability of disc for still frame display and the tapes themselves are subject to wear and degradation.

A videodisc is read by a laser head which moves radially over the surface of the disc. Access times are limited only by the response time of the particular disc player in use, the efficiency of software control and the time taken for the read head to move to the correct position. Maximum access times typically quoted are three seconds over the surface of a videodisc. Careful disc layout, with logically connected sequences laid out close to each other can result in access times of fractions of a second.

Videodisc access is very accurate. Any frame can be pin-pointed, which is important, as missing the desired frame by one frame is as bad as missing it by a hundred. Nearly right, for this purpose, is not good enough.

However, this accuracy is also vital for the segmentation of moving video. In applications involving the study of intricate human behaviour such as language use, manual or physical skills, behavioural interactions or non-verbal communication, it may be useful or essential to be able to break down the behaviour to be studied into its component parts or stages. The designer may then find that $\frac{1}{25}$ second accuracy is barely enough to capture some fleeting and delicate visual or linguistic messages.

Moving video pictures may appear to be in very sharp focus. However, when you freeze on one of the twenty-five frames which make up one second of moving footage, the individual image may well be blurred. For example, a vehicle travelling at 60 miles per hour will move more than three feet in $\frac{1}{25}$ second, and a person engaging in animated conversation may well move several inches. In each case, a blurred freeze-frame will result, as it does if you try to take photographs of moving objects with a camera using a slow shutter speed such as $\frac{1}{25}$ second.

Audio

A laservision disc has two sound channels which can give stereo sound (if the system is capable of reproducing it), or two separate sound tracks which can be accessed individually. Possible training uses of the two sound tracks are: commentaries in different languages, different levels of work, or different lessons exploiting the video material. Using both sound tracks also increases the number of minutes of sound available from the disc. Sound is only available when the videodisc is in normal speed forward play. Effectively this means that a maximum of either 36 or 72 minutes of audio is available, depending on whether the two audio tracks are different or not. You must bear in mind, however, that if the second audio track is used to carry 'extra' sound rather than alternative sound designed to fit the video sequence held on that part of the disc, this sound cannot be accompanied by a video sequence when used as part of your lesson. The screen will, therefore have to display some sort of text or graphic output from the computer during such sound sequences.

This facility to store extra sound on the second audio track can be very useful. Suppose, for example, you wish to display one or several screens of text with an audio commentary or explanation. The usual approach would be to 'hold' the text screens on the videodisc for as long as the audio requires. That is to say, if 15 seconds of audio are required over a text screen, you will need to have 375 video frames of the same text screen on the videodisc in order to give these 15 seconds of associated audio. If there were some other way of storing the required audio, there would be no reason why one text screen should take up more than one videodisc frame.

This waste of precious disc space can be avoided by providing text screens from the computer and storing the audio on the second audio track. Not only does this save videodisc space, it also extends the design possibilities by allowing you to use the same text screen with different audio sequences.

COMPUTER TOOLS

Digital storage

We will not go into much detail here about the possibilities of using one of the audio tracks for digital information, as this is more properly dealt with as a technical rather than educational discussion. For the purposes of the designer, however, the principal advantage of digital information stored on one audio track of the videodisc is the amount of information which can be stored and accessed in this way — over 1000 times more information than can be stored on a floppy disc.

The disadvantage of digital information stored on the audio track is that it is permanent. Unlike files stored on computer discs, which can be corrected, updated or changed at any time, information burned on to the videodisc is permanent, unchanging and unchangeable. This is an important consideration for a number of reasons. First, information stored on the videodisc can never be updated to keep pace with changing situations. Second, control programs stored on the videodisc cannot be adapted to accommodate possible changes in use of the videodisc. Also, no refining or error correction is possible after disc mastering is complete. The very fact that enormous quantities of information can be stored on a videodisc means that the task of checking the information for errors of fact or spelling is enormously increased, and the permanent nature of the optical disc as a storage medium means that correction of such errors cannot be done after disc pressing. Nor, of course, is it possible to make alterations in data files in order to adapt or alter the use of the disc.

Text Overlay

Most interactive video configurations allow text and graphics from the computer to be overlaid on to still or moving video. Text can be displayed over still frames or moving sequences, as well as in the form of whole screens of computer generated text or segments of computer-aided learning interspersed between video sequences.

Whenever text is to be displayed over video, some thought should be given to its clarity and visibility. If very clear text is required, as with foreign language subtitles, questions or commentaries, it can be on a background strip of some contrasting colour so that the words will stand out against the video background. There may be times, however, when information should be available but not obtrusive. For example, you may wish to have a reminder of what keys are operative, without unduly distracting the user from the content of the programme. It may then be useful to display the required information without a backing strip so that it may be read fairly easily if needed, but does not distract.

Because overlaid text is generated by the computer, it can only be displayed on that area of the screen which the computer uses for text, usually 80 columns by 25 lines. The border surrounding this text area cannot be used for overlaid text so that, for example, sub-titles cannot be displayed at the very bottom of the screen.

It is possible, however, to overlay the whole screen with a solid block of colour by setting the border and the text screen to the same colour, and this can be useful if you wish to play some audio without the associated video picture being visible.

Another consideration is the size of text to be used. There is often a choice of 40 or 80 column mode. This decision will be made according to the amount of textual information to display, the overall layout of the screen, the length of sub-titles required, the amount of free space to be left on the screen in the interests of clarity and how many characters are required for a particular piece of text. It is important, however, to keep a pleasing screen layout without constant changing of text mode or colours.

The importance of not displaying too much text on the screen at any one time cannot be overstressed: reading text from a computer screen is not the same as reading from paper and what would be perfectly acceptable amounts of printed text will look overcrowded, messy and confusing on screen. Spaces on a computer screen will not cost you money, unlike blank paper in printed material.

One important aspect of the use of computer-generated text is the choice of colour and reverse video or blinking effects. It is wise to become familiar with the text and background colour combinations allowed by your computer and to spend some time investigating the effect of various colour combinations. One point to bear in mind is the relative importance of textual information on screen. One piece of text may be of major importance, requiring the learner's complete attention while another on the same screen is designed to provide support to which the learner may refer if needed. In such circumstances the major piece of information could appear in a bold colour while the subordinate text appears in a more unobtrusive shade.

There may be a need to emphasize a changing part of the screen display. Here, the standout colour can move to different parts of the screen, either in response to some learner input or timed to do so by the program.

The techniques of standout colours or reverse video or blinking effects can also be used to help to overcome the 'screen blindness' which often seems to affect users of CAL systems.

Graphics Overlay

Graphics overlay is essentially similar to text overlay. It can either be generated by using graphics or other characters from the computer's character set, or by using a graphics package or programming to produce a much wider range of effects. Just like text, graphics cannot appear on the border of the screen.

Graphics overlay can be used to box off, frame or conceal parts of the video picture. It can be used to highlight with a circle, an arrow, a frame or some other symbol, a particular part of the screen, or to simulate a zoom in on a particular area, or to present information in graphical form. Care should be taken, however, not to indulge in flashy graphic effects just for the sake of it.

The instructional design of an IV package should not be determined by technological criteria — the quality of the learning experience it provides is its whole raison d'être and the major criterion whereby it will be judged. But it is worth considering whether it is worth spending the time programming extravagant graphic effects, which can be very costly in both computer memory and programming time.

Computer Sound

Although sound generated from a standard computer can be very limited compared to the audio possibilities available from the videodisc, there are useful things which can be done with it. It can be used, for example, to draw attention to the appearance of an important screen message.

Another possible exploitation of sound is to prevent incorrect use of the keyboard. If the wrong key is pressed, for example, or the right key is pressed for too long, a discreet sound will draw the user's attention to it, causing them to release it.

Interaction

The key to all computer use, and particularly learning applications, is interaction between the user and the system. A vitally important part of the design of any CAL program is the user interface and the decisions which must be made about how the learner will communicate with the system and how the system is programmed to respond. This question can be broken down as:

    (a) tasks required of the learner;

    (b) how the learner will respond to and communicate with the system — choice of appropriate input methods and devices;

    (c) motivation;

    (d) response analysis;

    (e) feedback;

    (f) remediation;

    (g) further progress.

Input devices

The designer's approach to the pedagogical requirements of the programme must be influenced by a knowledge of different input devices. These include:
- a mouse
- tracker ball
- a joystick
- a light pen
- a touch sensitive screen
- bar code reader
- keyboard

(a) Mouse
A mouse is a small device with a rubber ball on the under side and one, two or three buttons on top, which is connected to the computer and which sits on the work surface where it can be moved about by the user. As it moves, the ball registers movement which is transmitted to a pointer on the screen. Clicking the buttons on the mouse can select menu options, control scrolling, pull down menus. alter the size of or select screen windows — in short, control most interactions with the system short of actually entering text.

(b) Tracker ball
A tracker ball is similar in concept to a mouse, except that the user controls screen movement of the pointer by directly moving the ball which is on the upper surface of the device.

(c) Joystick
The joystick is another device which allows intuitive movements on screen by mimicking the action of the cursor movement keys. Joysticks also have one or more 'fire' buttons which assume the function of the space bar or enter key to allow choice or decision making.

(d) Light-pen
A light-pen looks very like a felt tip pen but is attached to the computer by a cable and allows movement of the cursor on screen simply by pointing at it. Decisions or choices usually have to be registered by using the keyboard.

(e) Touch sensitive screen
The touch sensitive screen also allows direct communication through the screen. In one form a solid state device generates an infra-red beam which scans the screen horizontally and vertically. The user's finger interrupts the scan and allows the system software to correlate position with screen layout and decision making.

(f) Bar code reader
A bar code reader is the device which is now commonly used in large supermarkets, warehouses and libraries to read information directly from the code printed on an

article. Such codes printed in a user manual accompanying a computer or interactive video learning programme can offer a useful way of inputting learner decisions.

(g) Keyboard

The most common input device, the keyboard, has been left until last as it offers a wider range of possibilities. However, these extended possibilities require careful thought about how, when and why to use them, and also pose many questions about the practical problems of implementation and the instructional philosophy you wish to employ.

If the learner is asked to type free-form answers there are many problems to consider and many questions to answer. Can the computer program recognize alternative correct answers? Can the program accept a fundamentally correct answer with a slight mis-spelling? Is it necessary, or even possible, to distinguish between a typing error caused by unfamiliarity with the keyboard and a genuine spelling mistake? At what point does a spelling mistake become a wrong answer? Can the word or words denoting the correct answer be picked up in the middle of a sentence? Will you demand a strict use of capital letters, punctuation, foreign accents? If not, how will you decide on acceptable levels of correctness? If the learning program involves giving numerical answers, what provision will you make for answers given in words as well as figures, and what degree of accuracy is required in the answer? These questions and many more will be dealt with in more detail later.

There are so many problems attached to the input of free-form answers that many CAL programs prefer not to take them on board. Instead, questions are asked and responses required which can be more easily handled by the computer. In this category are multiple choice, true or false, and matching questions. In all cases, you should base your choice of user input on what is appropriate for the learning experience you are designing. Once again it is vitally important to establish a co-operative working relationship with the software designer in which it is clearly understood by all parties that the design of an educational application should be methodology-led and not technology-led.

This means either of two things. First, the design should not be affected by what can be easily programmed or implemented. You should not choose multiple choice questions because they are easily programmed, but because they suit the style and content of your programme. Second, the design should not employ technical fire-works just for the sake of it. It may be possible to include elaborate graphics or other advanced techniques, but it is only worthwhile if it positively enhances the quality of the learning experience.

Computer control

All the above resources can be subjected to judgment by the computer program. Your program will set up interactions between the learner and the system which can be monitored and acted on by the program.

The first stage in this process of interaction is the the initial learning situation which is set up by the program, going from introductory screens to the first stimulus and request for learner reaction and input. The program can then respond to the learner's input in a variety of ways depending on the learning strategy employed.

For some applications it will be appropriate to allow the learner to request, explicitly, some progress or movement to another learning sequence or a free browsing facility. For others, the system's judgment of the user's response can bring appropriate feedback or, if the response is considered unsatisfactory, remediation.

The feedback may be in the form of explicit comment or congratulation to the learner followed by progress to another stage or an offer of movement to another stage. More appropriately in interactive video, it is possible to show the consequences of a decision by taking the learner to a follow-up sequence determined by the response which has just been made.

It should be pointed out that computer analysis of learner responses need not, indeed often should not, be confined to right or wrong. There may be more than one appropriate response or a whole spectrum of appropriateness. The program may then allow different learners different paths through the learning experience. There will be more discussion later of branching programs and the extent to which they can genuinely allow a wide variety of different learning paths.

Remediation can range from simply asking the learner to view the sequence again to a much more sophisticated analysis of the learner's score or success rate and transfer to a remedial learning activity.

All cases of feedback or remediation, however, depend on the program's ability to analyse the learner's responses. The principle here is that it is possible for a program to recognize and act upon any anticipated response. This is far easier said than done, and will be dealt with in detail later.

There will also be substantial discussion later of the relative benefits of authoring languages and programming languages in the field of interactive video. Whether it is decided to adopt the authoring approach or the programming approach, it may well be worth the trouble to learn and work with an authoring language with reasonable response analysis facilities even if only to learn to understand the principles of response matching and anticipation.

THE DESIGN PROCESS

Analysis of Training Needs

(a) Hard Skills

Hard skills are procedural skills, such as those involved in operating or servicing machinery. It is a presumption that there are clearly correct ways to perform and that generally this performance can be taught, monitored and assessed objectively. IV programmes to teach such skills generally have few problems in the area of testing, feedback and assessment.

(b) Soft Skills

Soft skills (or 'squishy' skills as they are sometimes called in the United States) fall in the area of inter-personal and communicative training. Sales, staff and customer relations, decision- making and interview skills from either side of the desk fall into this area.

What probably characterizes a soft skills programme more definitely than any other is the fact that any assessment must have a degree of subjectivity.

Problems relating to the design of soft skills training spring essentially from the subjective nature of the assessment: because the skills are so subtle and complex, the designers are often led to a simplification of the possible responses and of the input required from the users. Thus soft skills programmes often show a trigger video sequence, and then offer three or four elemental multiple choice questions. This is often presented as three or four different ways to respond to the trigger scenario. When one is chosen, some feedback is usually given on screen, often in the form of gentle approval or reproof, and some additional advice about what might have been decided. There is often an opportunity to try the other possible responses before continuing with the programme.

Notice that what is described here falls somewhat short of the infinite number of pathways through a programme which one often sees invoked as a particular strength of IV and CBT courseware. There are severe limitations to branching within an IV programme (see pp114-115).

(c) Concepts

Programmes designed to teach concepts will generally lend themselves quite favourably to IV techniques. The designer can call upon moving video, still photographs and computer generated screens (or a mixture) to present information and illustrate ideas, and the analysis of text or numerical inputs can now be done very flexibly using well understood CBT techniques.

In addition, it is possible to incorporate feedback sequences which can use video or sequences of still frames to show the consequences of answers in a much more concrete way than can be done using more conventional training media.

Existing Training Problems

The discussion of subject matter will clearly affect the content of courseware and your decision about whether the required training is suitable for an IV solution. Here are some key questions to answer, with, in some cases, an indication of the kind of courseware or training solution which has been produced in response to them.

- Is the subject matter per se indigestible and boring? Do trainees find it difficult to concentrate in a normal training environment? (Financial procedures. European Community regulations)

- Does the teaching require a very clear view of a process which it is difficult to demonstrate in normal group situations? (Electrical wiring. Circuit board manufacture.)

- Is the teaching difficult to simulate properly because of danger or cost? (Oil platform safety measures. Firefighting.)

- Does the training involve employees or managers who cannot easily be spared from their work? (Open access learning centres.)

Target Groups

Careful thought about your target groups will affect the style, presentation and choice of delivery system for your courseware. Once again, here are some key questions with some suggested responses.

(a) Who are your target groups? Are they homogenous?What is their previous educational background? Are they of similar status? How old are they?

(b) What do they know already? Do your programmes need to specify a particular level of pre-existing knowledge? Are they for beginners/intermediate/ advanced users? How will you tell which is which? Will you need to include a pretest in your courseware, or will there be some other non-IV based sifting procedure?

(c) What are the existing general skills of target groups? Are they keyboard literate and are they happy to use keyboards? (In the UK keyboard skills are sometimes felt to be beneath the dignity of managerial grades, and if this is a factor in your organization then maybe you will need to consider a mouse as your input device.) Will the system be used in public places by the general public? If so, perhaps a touch screen is an option to be explored.

(d) What assumptions or knowledge exist about their preferred learning styles? Will you be teaching in an area in which people might feel embarrassed to perform in public? If so, perhaps you will need to present your programme to be used on a one-to-one basis. If your target audience is managerial or supervisory, might they feel reluctant to be seen to lack knowledge? Again, you may need to design programmes for single users or, at least, groups of trainees of similar status.

If soft skills are to be taught, is the interaction between users and system less useful than between groups working together using the IV courseware as a way of stimulating discussion? Consider producing courseware which will trigger beneficial group interactions. Do your target users prefer to be given a clearly defined programme of instruction with clearly defined goals and feedback? If so, your courseware may well tend towards programmed learning styles and frequent performance testing. Do your target users prefer a degree of choice and control over their own learning process? Is exploratory learning an appropriate option? If so, consider how you can promote learner independence without sacrificing the sense of purposeful learning.

Goal Setting

If you are trying to teach skills, what will users be able to do after completion of the programmes that they could not do before? How will this be tested to your satisfaction and to theirs?

If you are trying to teach concepts or knowledge, there should still be a clear learning outcome which can be demonstrated to trainers and trained alike.

If you are designing an exploratory programme, particularly if its aim is affective, that is, intended to change peoples' feelings or attitudes, then the whole area of goal setting becomes less concrete. However, one way or another, there should be some way of demonstrating some gain or change to the participants.

Programme Design

Flowcharting

It is essential that you have a clear and clearly documented plan of what you are going to do, and it might take the form of a flowchart.

A flowchart is a programmer's tool intended to give an unequivocal diagram of the logical functioning of a process or program. Its function is to give a clear picture of the sometimes very complex routes involved. Flowcharting is one, although by no means the only, approach to software design. When used, the flowchart must be totally logical.

Now for the crucial questions: does the person designing the courseware have the training, ability or skill to draw up a correct flowchart which would explain the design to a programmer better than it can be done in words or in a script? Can such a flowchart be produced as quickly and as efficiently as a trained programmer would do it?

If the answer to these questions is yes, then go ahead with the flowchart. The designer clearly has some software design training and the production of a flowchart is probably the most efficient path to programme visualization. If not, then your course of action depends on who is going to produce the software.

If your answer to the questions is no, and if you are going to use an authoring language to produce software yourself, then draw up a flowchart if it makes you happy and if you feel it will help you to define and think more clearly about your design.

However, if your answer is no and if you are going to hand over your specification to another person to program for you, then drawing up a flowchart may prove to be a waste of time, because this person is undoubtedly going to have to spend a great deal of time with you finding out what the flowchart is supposed to mean.

It may be more efficient to produce documentation in some other form as a basis for discussion between you and the programmer, which will lead to the production of a correct functional specification by someone with the appropriate training.

Programme Visualization

Programme visualization involves a process of progressively more detailed descriptions of what will actually happen on screen. At each stage, be prepared to discuss the work with people who can make useful contributions. They should be people with varying backgrounds who can give useful feedback from different points of view. You could try to discuss the design at each stage with some or all of the following:

   (a) Someone with similar experience and knowledge to your own. Regard this as useful brainstorming and feedback, as it is easy to get carried away with the excitement of working with a new and powerful medium.
   (b) A subject expert, to make sure that you have committed no significant factual errors.

(c) A trainer or teacher experienced in this domain, to make sure that the approach it is intended to adopt is appropriate and likely to be effective.

(d) An instructional designer, to get useful feedback on the use of the medium.

(e) A software specialist, who will first give an assessment of the practicability of the design, and subsequently work with you to produce a correct flowchart and functional specification.

(f) A video specialist who can advise on the feasibility of obtaining the video you need.

The Detailed Design Process

Stage One

Begin with a written overview, using diagrams if you find them helpful, of what the programme is required to do. Then begin laying out a document which describes each step as the user will see it.

The order in which end users will use the programme is not necessarily the most logical order in which to design it. It can often be more sensible to begin with an overview of the central core of the learning experience, and then to work backwards to refine how the user will get there and forwards to refine how he or she will continue and exit.

Put together a simply written description of what you want your learners to do. You may wish this to be in the form of an extended treatment laid out in headed columns on the page, for example:

Video	Audio	Computer

If you have a number of different activities planned, then you should have this overview description for each of them. Continue in this way until you have fairly broad documentation for each separate strand of your programme. Then stop, take stock and consult your advisory team.

Stage Two

In the light of these discussions, begin to expand your written design. The number of times you need to re-iterate this documentation/feedback process will depend largely on the complexity of your design. The final stage however, will involve a completely documented central programme with all sequences, interactions, branches and answer analysis in place.

You may find that as you go deeper into this design process, you need to adopt some convention within your team to enable all concerned to understand exactly what is meant by the documents. This is easier said than done with a medium which combines so many resources. The sort of things you may have to find ways of documenting are:

- play video sequence
- audio track on
- audio track off
- freeze frame until user responds
- play timed succession of still frames

- freeze frame for fixed period
- slow motion (forward/reverse)
- fast play (forward/reverse)
- multiple choice question
- matching question
- user input
- anticipated correct answer(s)
- acceptable answer
- anticipated incorrect answer(s)
- unanticipated answer
- text overlaid on video
- text screen

User Interface and the entry to programmes.

At some point in this refinement of the central programme design, things that you include will begin to have an effect on your thinking about how users will enter the programme. You will then work backwards to design the user interface. Considerations here will include:

- What will the first screen look like when the user switches on? Will on-screen instructions appear to allow users to continue or will it continue automatically to the next stage?

- Do you want there to be any differentiation between experienced users and first-time users? Do experienced users have any more choices, or are they allowed to bypass instructions which are compulsory to first timers? Remember that explanations which are gratefully received the first time may interfere with or slow down user choices for the experienced.

A good principle to adopt is that a good CBT or IV programme should certainly offer its users no fewer possibilities than would be available in print materials, and that one of the features available in print materials and taken for granted by us all is the ability to skip unwanted material.

Entry to programmes for inexperienced users
Inexperienced users will require some or all of the following, not all of which will necessarily be given as on-screen instructions. Printed documentation or a keyboard template may be the best way for some information.

(a) Clear and lucid instructions about how to load and move through the programme.
(b) Clear and comprehensible instructions about:
- What they are required to do by the teaching programme: ie what kind of learning behaviour is required of them.
- How to interact with the system, ie which keys to press, how to move forwards and backwards and how to enter responses.

(c) Clear instructions about how to exit from the programme.

(d) Enough on-screen help to be able to work with confidence within a very short time.

Entry to programmes for experienced users.

Choices which should be offered to the experienced user:

(a) Select a point of entry in order to recap or revise.

(b) Resume at the point the lesson was previously left.

(c) Avoid detailed explanations intended for inexperienced users.

(d) Have help available if required.

Features which should be available to all users

(a) The ability to exit when required. Do not lock users into programmes, especially if they are likely to find them difficult.

(b) The ability to exercise choice and control over pace of learning.

(c) The ability to browse and explore wherever possible.

(d) Freedom from unnecessary or distracting graphic effects and insulting 'humorous' feedback.

Video

At an early stage during the process of courseware design, the required video must be specified. You should consider some or all of the following:

(a) Does your organization have existing video footage which is appropriate and which exists in an acceptable format?

(b) Can you obtain usable material already pressed to videodisc?

(c) If there is no suitable material for your definitive programme, can you lay your hands on a CAV disc with semi-suitable material on it for experimental design and programming?

Bear in mind that these are 'second best' options, and that video material which has been edited for linear viewing as videotape is likely to be quite unsuitable for use in an interactive programme on disc.

If, as is likely, you decide you must shoot dedicated video for your programme, you must make the following decisions:

(a) How many minutes of footage do you need?

(b) Do you have in-house shooting and editing facilities of the right standard?

(c) What locations are required? Remember, the more locations, the more expense.

(d) Will you need actors to perform dramatized scenarios?

(e) Can you shoot processes, demonstrations or even dramatizations using people or locations within your organization?

There is an important issue here of authenticity. If you consider it important that users can identify closely with the people in video sequences in the courseware, it may be important to have authentic material. The dichotomy here is between actors, who can produce a dramatically satisfactory performance, but who may be perceived by a specialist audience as behaving inappropriately, and 'real' people who clearly understand the words and actions they are performing, but whose performance may be stilted and awkward.

It may be valuable to think of any TV drama you have seen which was placed in a setting you know a good deal about. Were you convinced by the actors, or was it quite clear to you as an expert that they understood little of the specialized vocabulary which the scriptwriter had put in their mouths? Failure to speak lines with understanding may be more likely to cause your target learners to switch off than a stilted performance by a genuine expert.

(f) Do your programmes require any particular elements to be provided by the video? Will you for example require large close-ups or particularly clear audio?

Storyboarding

Storyboarding is a tool often used in the video/film world to give a grasp of the visual material to be produced. Essentially, a storyboard is like a strip cartoon with sketched representations of the principal story points.

Storyboards are by no means always used, and it is perfectly possible to produce a clear specification for the video requirement without one.

Other tools which are perfectly adequate are a script with sufficient indication of the visuals required or a treatment with a written description of the shots running alongside the script or voice- over.

In any case, the precise content of the finished video will be affected by the actual conditions on the ground during the video shoot.

Again, the best way of controlling the finished shape of each element in the IV production process is for key members of the IV team to work side by side throughout the process. If any commissioned organization is unwilling to allow you to be involved in the production process, our advice is to seek another, more co-operative organization.

Branching

The videodisc is an extremely dense storage medium. It is commonly thought of as having such enormous storage capacity that it offers unlimited design resources, and it is not unusual to see descriptions of IV which claim that branching programmes can be produced which will allow users an unlimited number of different paths through them.

While this may sometimes be technically true, it must be recognized that there can be severe limitations on the branching possibilities of the medium.

The available spectrum of resources is 54 000 still frames or 36 minutes of moving video. If the whole of your video resource is made up of still frames, then it is true that these 54 000 possibilities can be arranged in ways which will indeed deliver more pathways than any one user is ever likely to be able to exhaust.

If, on the other hand, you are making use of moving video in, for example, a customer-handling training package, then your room for manoeuvre may be severely restricted.

Let us assume for the sake of calculation that your video is arranged in 10-second sequences. Each second of moving footage requires 25 video frames (or 30 if you are working in NTSC). Each 10-second clip will therefore occupy 250 frames, and a PAL/SECAM disc will allow you 216 such clips, while in NTSC you will have 180 sequences available.

A standard use of branching will involve an introductory sequence followed by a decision point with perhaps a three element multiple choice question. If each of these decision points leads to a ten second video sequence, then one level into the courseware you will have used four of your available sequences. If each of these leads in turn to another three sequences, level two will have used eleven sequences. The progression will look like this:

Level	Video required	Cumulative Total
Intro Sequence	1 video segment	1 video segment
Level 1	3 segments	4 segments
Level 2	9 segments	13 segments
Level 3	27 segments	40 segments
Level 4	81 segments	121 segments
Level 5	243 segments	364 segments

That is to say, a programme designed on diverging pathways will run out of video resource after four decision points. This means either that the programme must be very cleverly designed to use the same clips in a large number of different contexts, or that the usability of the video must be extended by having different audio tracks, or the programme must keep bringing users back to the same nodal decision points. This last is the approach which is most often used and it is quite clearly some distance from the unlimited learning pathways which are often promised.

TESTING AND QUESTIONING TECHNIQUES

In order to implement a programme a courseware designer may may use an authoring language or may work with a programmer. Different authoring languages have different strengths and different ways of analysing and responding to common question types. Programming is a more flexible process, but in this case the courseware designer must be able to specify to the programmer what is required and how users are likely to behave while working the courseware. Both authoring and programming can produce well implemented solutions, as long as the designer has thought clearly about the questions which are to be asked and the responses which may be made.

Teaching or Testing

There are two main reasons for asking questions in your programmes: one is to teach or train and the other is to test what has been taught. The distinction can sometimes be a fine one, but a simple example can illustrate the difference.

Suppose the objective of a module is to teach a particular calculation technique. At the end of the module, you would very likely wish to include some problems for the trainee to solve in order to assess how well the trainee has mastered the target skill.

If the test score is unsatisfactory you will need to consider why. It may be that the trainee has failed to master the skill and will need to be routed to a remedial track or required to repeat the module. Alternatively (and this is certainly the case if large numbers of the target group are returning unsatisfactory scores) your programme may be at fault and require revision.

On the other hand, the objective of the module may be to train users in mental arithmetic skills, possibly against the clock. In this case, you may wish to throw calculations on the screen with a time limit for each solution. In this case, you are providing the opportunity for practice of the target skill in order to establish mastery, rather than trying to establish if it has been mastered when working through a previous exercise.

Keyboard Entry

Multiple Choice

The most frequent type of questioning or testing in CBT or IV programmes is multiple choice questions (MCQs). There are a number of sub-types of multiple choice questions:

Example (a)

What is the capital of France?
(a)   Bonn
(b)   London
(c)   Paris
(d)   Copenhagen

Note that in this case there is one correct answer and three incorrect, and that there is no attempt to trick the learner by the inclusion of a 'distractor'.

Example (b)   Question with Distractor

What is the capital of West Germany?
(a)   Bonn
(b)   Paris
(c)   Bern
(d)   Rome

In this case the distraction comes from the sound similarity between Bonn and Bern.

Example (c)   Question with multiple distractors

What is the capital of West Germany?
(a)   Bonn
(b)   Bern
(c)   Berlin
(d)   Basle

Here all the alternative answers begin with a B, and in addition to the aural distraction supplied by Bern, there is both an aural distraction and one of plausibility in Berlin.

Example (d) Complete the statement

The stopping distance for a car travelling at 30 miles an hour is:

(a)   60 feet
(b)   75 feet
(c)   90 feet
(d)   100 feet

Notice that with this sort of questioning or testing of factual knowledge, we are simply expecting users to select a response which is correct in terms of the question.

In areas such as the testing of language, it is possible to break down types of MCQs further. A learner of English language, for example, might receive the following types of MCQ:

Example (e)

Here, each suggested response is in isolation a correct use of English language, but only one of them shows acceptable understanding of the question.

'What will you have as a starter?' asked the waiter.
(a)   Champagne cocktail
(b)   Roast beef
(c)   Red wine
(d)   Prawn cocktail

Example (f)

In this case, once again, each suggested answer is a correct use of the English language, but this time only one is grammatically correct in the context of the question.

'We would have been on time if the train...
(a)   ...was late.'
(b)   ...wasn't late.'
(c)   ...had not been late.'
(d)   ...isn't late.'

Example (g)

In the following question in which only one of the responses is correct in any circumstances.

'I asked them to...
(a)   ...sit down.'
(b)   ...seating down.

(c)   ...be sitting.
(d)   ...seated down.

Practical considerations in the design of MCQs in CBT and IV are normally fairly simple. Most users will understand that they must enter the letter of the correct answer. Remember, however, that you must design for as many foreseeable variations as possible.

Upper case and lower case letters can be completely different characters to a computer. Don't forget to allow for the use of either or both. Decide if the computer should accept the response immediately or if the trainee should type the letter and then press <enter>. If you choose the latter, the user will be able to have second thoughts.

The occasional user will try to enter the text of the chosen answer or (which is more difficult to allow for) a word or a sentence. For example, 'The capital of West Germany is Bonn'. You can allow for this by displaying a screen message such as 'Type a, b, c or d', either as a constant line at the bottom of the screen or in response to any attempt to type anything other than those single characters.

Take care here — if your response analysis is not efficient, peculiar things can happen. Make sure that the programming is set up to look for a single letter entry only and to send an advisory message if the user tries to enter more. Otherwise this sort of thing can happen.

Example (h)

What is the capital of West Germany?
(a)   Bonn
(b)   Bern
(c)   Berlin
(d)   Basle

The user correctly selects response (a) Bonn, but tries to type the word Bonn. The software is looking for the letter (a) but receives the letter B as the initial letter of the word Bonn. A poorly written program will disregard the last three letters, accept B as the intended answer and give appropriate feedback for answer (b), which might be, 'No, Bonn is the capital of West Germany'.

The whole dialogue, therefore, might go like this:

Q   'What is the capital of West Germany?'
A   'B(onn)'
Feedback   'No, Bonn is the capital of West Germany.'

This sort of program will only distract and irritate trainees.

Disadvantages of Multiple Choice
Multiple choice questions are considered pedagogically unsound by many people. They feel that such questions presents several incorrect answers for the learner's consideration. A conscientious user will think carefully about each possibility before

making a decision. In the first instance, therefore, we are exposing learners to three times as many incorrect answers as correct ones, and encouraging them to think as carefully about the incorrect ones as about the correct ones. In the case of questions which actually present answers which are quite wrong in isolation as well as in context, we are re-inforcing incorrect forms in the learner's mind with all the authority bestowed on them by the computer screen and printed text.

Another weakness of this approach is that multiple choice questions also encourage a 'reverse' strategy for selecting correct answers. Where learners do not immediately know the right answer, they will normally proceed by eliminating first the most unlikely response, then the next most unlikely and so on.

This sort of selection by elimination may be precisely the ability you are trying to train your target audience to acquire. If so, then it is a perfectly legitimate questioning technique; if not, you should be aware that your students are likely to approach it in the wrong frame of mind and not derive much benefit from it. Generations of school-children brought up with multiple-choice tests have referred to them as 'guessing tests': you should seriously consider whether the tests provided for your motivated, mature and intelligent adult audience are substantially any better.

Why, then, in view of the serious disadvantages attached to them, are MCQs so frequently used in CBT and IV courseware?

Sadly, it is fairly clear that we are dealing here with a combination of technological difficulties and reduced expectations. Multiple choice questions are very easy to program and they offer a simple solution to a number of complex problems associated with user inputs to computer- based learning systems.

They eliminate the need, for example, to come to terms with the complex decisions involved in designing for free form text input, some of which we discuss below. The multiple choice question limits users' possible responses to four or five; spelling mistakes and typing errors can very easily be trapped and an answer of some type can always be given however ignorant the learner. If multiple-choice tests are to be scored, even pure guesswork will result in some limited correct answering, unless some form of compensating calculation is included in the scoring.

It is not entirely unfair to say that MCQs are the offspring of the punch-card and the computer, and that the principle reason for their emergence as a major form of testing was ease and speed of marking. The dominant use of this form of questioning in the first era of CBT seemed to establish it as the CBT norm, and most authoring languages contain MCQ questioning routines as a fundamental facility. So a vicious circle has become established: MCQs are used because they are easy to design and program - therefore CBT programs are based on them, most authoring systems offer them and most designers employ them — therefore trainee designers use them because they model themselves on standard practice.

Eliminating the guesswork element in MCQ Scoring

This can be done fairly simply. Assuming a test of twenty questions, each one with four elements of which one is clearly the correct answer, a visitor from Alpha Centauri with no understanding of the printed questions would, according to the law of probabilities, correctly guess one in four, ie five out of twenty questions. This may be good for motivation but is not much use for testing or assessing acquired learning benefits. To compensate for this guessing effect, award three points for a correct answer and minus one for an incorrect one. Your Alpha Centauri student will, therefore, score 15 points for the 5 correct answers and minus 15 for the 15 incorrect ones, giving the appropriate mark of zero.

Multiple choice as a signaller of decisions

It is especially true of IV courseware designed for personal skills training such as management and sales, that MCQs are often not used to test the trainee's ability to pick out a single correct answer.   These programmes may, for instance, present a dramatized video sequence to which the user is required to respond by choosing from a number of plausible courses of action, none of which need necessarily be presented as totally correct or incorrect.

For example, a management training course might ask the user to assume the role of a middle manager faced with an angry phone call from a client whose order has not arrived despite assurances from his company's despatch department. The choices offered might then be:

(a)   Apologise and say it's not your fault.
(b)   Angrily tell the customer not to swear at you.
(c)   Apologise, say you will look into it and call the customer back.
(d)   Say it's not your responsibility and offer to put the customer through to the despatch department.

Some responses are obviously preferable to others. Here, response (c) is probably the best and response (b) is clearly unacceptable, but there is no clearly defined line between right and wrong answers. Feedback would probably take the form of a video sequence showing the customer's possible reaction to the manager's decision and also, perhaps, some overlaid text which would add further comments. A user choosing option (d), for example, might be shown a customer only partly satisfied and still annoyed by what might be seen as the user's attempt to pass the buck. Text overlay might amplify this point and advise the trainee to take more personal responsibility. Even trainees choosing the 'best' response (c) might receive further advice in the form of a reminder that promises to call back must always be kept.

The guesswork element does not come into a programme of this type, as there is no single correct answer, and if it required to score responses then the scores awarded should reflect the scale of correctness determined by the subject expert.

Concealed multiple choice

There are various ways of concealing multiple choice questions, either for the purpose of reducing some of their disadvantages or in order to introduce variety.

The best known variation in computing is of course the menu, often with the highlight bar for entering choices rather than the typing of numbers. Notice that here the purpose of the menu which takes you into a word processing program, or, indeed, a CBT program, is not testing. It is a way of presenting a highly complicated 'route' in the form of a number of simple choices.

It is also clear that the WIMP environments - windows, icons (pictorial representations), mouse and pointers - which are now available for most microcomputers -

merely offer similar multiple choice option routines in graphical form and driven by movements of the mouse rather than movement keys.

Other restricted question forms
Restricting the possible responses a user can make is desirable if it is important to reduce programming complexity. There are a number of variations.

Matching
A matching form of the capital city questions might read like this:

Example (i)
Match the countries and their capital cities:

1	France	a	London
2	West Germany	b	Paris
3	United Kingdom	c	Rome
4	Italy	d	Bonn

There is the advantage here that no incorrect information is printed on screen and that four times as much information is being tested as in the simple multiple choice question.

Rank Order
Another form of restricted questioning is requiring trainees to enter a list in rank order. This can often be quite appropriate as a way of testing numerical understanding as well as other kinds of learning.

Example (j)

Arrange these countries in order of population, with the largest first:

(a) Sweden	1..........
(b) West Germany	2..........
(c) France	3..........
(d) United Kingdom	4..........

Numerical Entry
Numerical entry, apart from responses to MCQs, is appropriate for learning programmes involving numerical calculation. There are authoring languages which offer very sophisticated calculation functions, not merely arithmetic, but drawing curves and calculating equations. In general, there are few problems in designing the response analysis for numerical entry. The main thing to look out for is possible variations in the likely format of the user's input.

First, there should be some way of establishing agreement as to the required accuracy of the answer — what level of approximation the program will accept, how many places of decimals are expected and so on. In every case, it should be clear to the user what is expected.

Second, you should allow for the possibility that the user may try to type the answer in words rather than figures. Either set the response analysis to accept both forms, or trap any typing of alphabetic characters and display a request for figures.

Free Text Entry

Designing CBT or IV programmes which will accept free form text entry is one of the most difficult and challenging things a courseware designer can be called upon to do. Effectively, the task is to anticipate every single possible response which might be arrived at by any of the people who might at any time use the programme. In addition, each of these responses requires appropriate feedback.

The standard definitions of artificial intelligence are illuminating here. Artificial intelligence is sometimes described as behaviour by a machine which would be indicative of intelligence if displayed by a human being. There is a vital point of practical motivation and learner psychology here. Users will not continue to make allowances for machines for very long. In effect, a CBT program presents the machine to the user as an omniscient, infinitely patient and infinitely wise individual tutor. But this is a cunningly assembled and benevolent deception. A CBT program could not be further from an individual learning experience: it is designed by a person who is remote from the learners, who probably does not know them as individuals or a group, who may work on another site or even for another company altogether.

As long as this deception works, then it is a beneficial one for the learner: the moment it is revealed as a deception by an inappropriate response, then the learner is demotivated. Quite simply, if an infinitely patient, all-knowing tutor treats you insensitively or responds with extreme stupidity it is bad enough, but if a machine behaves in this way it is intolerable.

It is unlikely that you will ever succeed 100 per cent in achieving perfect response analysis for free form text entry. Indeed, however experienced and knowledgeable the designer may be, it will impossible to anticipate and give suitable feedback or prompts for every response. If it is required to do more than merely accept one set of responses and reject all others it will be necessary to gain experience of unanticipated correct or partially correct answers by trialling programmes with a representative sample of the target group.

So, what pitfalls can arise from even a very simple question?

For example, for the question 'what is an elephant?', the response should reasonably contain the two keywords 'animal' and 'trunk'.

Example (k)

Computer: What is an elephant?
User: An animal.
Computer: Wrong, an elephant is an animal with a trunk.

This exchange is very crude. The question is asked, the two keywords are sought, and if only one is present there is no attempt to prompt for the other one. The user in this exchange will rightly feel unfairly treated. Now let us see how this can be improved by giving a suitable prompt.

Example (l)

Computer: What is an elephant?
User: An animal.

Computer: What kind of animal?
User: It has a trunk.

Note that this last response only contains one of the key words. The program will therefore respond:

        Wrong, an elephant is an animal with a trunk.

The user, a human being, remembers saying animal and feels no need to repeat the word. The computer, on the other hand, has been programmed to look for the two words animal and trunk, and unless there is some way of getting it to store a partly right but incomplete response and add it to subsequent responses, you may get the above unsatisfactory response.

This can also be improved with reasonably sophisticated anticipation. A much more satisfactory exchange would be:

Example (m)

Computer: What is an elephant?
User: An animal.
Computer: What kind of animal?
User: It has a trunk.
Computer   Correct.

In order to allow this kind of response, the program must store the first of the two keywords, prompt for the second, and add the two together.

As well as allowing you to specify what is required in answers, the program should also allow you to specify what is prohibited.

Example (n)

Computer: What is an elephant?
User: An animal without a trunk.
Computer   Correct, an elephant is an animal with a trunk.

Since the response contains the two keywords animal and trunk, the program has accepted a response which means the opposite of what is required. One solution is to specify animal and trunk as required components of the correct answer but to reject any answer containing animal, trunk and the words not or without.

Pitfall number three involves the user making an unanticipated correct response:
'An elephant is a pachyderm. '
'An elephant is a large grey animal living in Africa and India. '

The solution is to anticipate as many answers as possible, and to trial programs so that you can pick up actual user responses. A line can always be drawn between reasonable anticipation and what is frankly impractical. Anticipating the responses of the freakish 1 per cent of users may require an unacceptable amount of time, so the designer should keep a sense of proportion.

Designers may well also find themselves devoting an unacceptable amount of time to anticipating the responses not of potential trainees, but of clients or other trainers and designers who may well do their best to defeat their program. For example, one computer program was designed for secondary school pupils learning French as a foreign language. The program asked pupils to enter their ages in French. Revisions had to be made to the program to allow for and give appropriate feedback to adults who were almost all entering absurd ages in an attempt to defeat the programming. No *bona fide* target user was ever observed entering a flippant or intentionally awkward response, and it took far longer to design suitable response matching to cope with responses by other users than for the genuine targets.

Pitfall number four is similar but involves the use of a synonym, equivalent word or reasonable alternative for all or part of the answer:

'An elephant is a creature with a trunk.'
'An elephant is a mammal with a trunk.'
'An elephant is an animal with tusks.'

Once again, anticipation and trialling will help, bearing in mind that you will at some stage reach a point of diminishing returns and will probably have to accept that an unacceptable amount of work is involved in coping with the last 1 per cent of possible responses.

There are a whole range of problems associated with spaces and the beginnings and ends of words. Suppose you ask users to give you the name of an old town, originally a Roman encampment, on the banks of the River Dee. The answer required is Chester. If your program is looking for the character string 'Chester' anywhere in the response, then what happens if the user gives the answer 'Manchester'?

One way of eliminating this possibility is to demand the string 'Chester' preceded by a space. This is fine if the user types in the sentence 'The name of this town is Chester'. However, if, as is more likely, the user merely types 'Chester', there is no space before the response. You can eliminate this problem by specifying a response beginning with the string 'Chester'.

The program must therefore be capable of accepting either a response starting with the string 'Chester' or containing the string '(Space)Chester'.

The next big problem is spelling and typing errors. This is not the place to go into a prolonged discussion of what constitutes a permissible level of errors, and you will no doubt have your own feelings about the issue. However, in our opinion, a good rule of thumb is to match the degree of accuracy expected in answers to the style and content of the learning program. In a program designed to teach or test correct written English, it is fair and appropriate to expect an accurately spelled response; in a program dealing with numerical processing or comprehension of concepts, accurate spelling may be quite irrelevant to your objectives or, indeed, interfere with them.

You should also consider whether the user of upper/lower case should be allowed for. Remember that to a computer upper case C and lower case c may be totally different characters, and if you want either to be acceptable, you must say so.

Another way of allowing for spelling mistakes is to specify a sequence of letters occurring anywhere in the answer. Suppose you ask a question requiring the answer 'encyclopaedia'. This is a word quite likely to give rise to spelling or typing errors. If you design your program to accept answers containing the string 'encyclo', then you eliminate the part of the word most likely to cause trouble. In many cases, having the help of someone who has extensive experience of teaching the target skills to a similar audience can assist in anticipating the kind of mistakes which are to be expected.

Only when an appropriate level of expectation or anticipation has been determined do authoring or programming come into play to implement the design requirements.

Pointing and indicating techniques

Pointing and indicating techniques use input devices such as the touch sensitive screen, light pen, tracker ball or mouse.

There is a considerable split amongst both users and designers between those who favour the keyboard, and those who advocate the use of pointing devices. In general, it is felt that those people who may be hostile to developing keyboard skills can be better reached by the use of some kind of pointer.

Such people break down into two main groups: those for whom keyboard skills are reckoned to be too complex, and those who consider keyboard use the mark of lower grade employees.

The main points are that the keyboard is likely to be the most straightforward device to work with, and that a decision to use any other device should be clearly taken in response to one of the following factors:

(a) Marked hostility to the keyboard by your intended target groups (eg senior managers).

(b) Significant lack of keyboard skills (or physical impairment) among your target groups (eg the physically handicapped).

(c) Circumstances of use which make a keyboard clearly inappropriate (eg a point of sale or information programme in a busy public place, such as an airport).

(d) A clear requirement by the teaching content of the programme (eg a need to make spatial or geographical inputs direct via a touch screen, or a need for intuitive and rapid manipulation of a small number of functions).

Once it has been decided to use a pointing device, bear in mind that you are mostly dealing with a variation of menu or multiple choice inputs.

You can reduce the surface similarity with these techniques by allowing users to select pictorial representations (or icons) rather than actual menus or numbered questions. However, it should be said that the actual mental processing which is possible for users is likely to be fairly limited, and that mental processing is desirable if substantial learning is to take place.

Pointing devices are very suitable for providing a very simple interface to programs — it is for this very reason that they are used to provide environment managers for the latest personal computers instead of the command-driven operating systems which preceded them.

The other main use for pointing techniques is in programmes where decisions are required based on the physical position or appearance of objects on the screen. It would be entirely appropriate to expect users to point to specific areas of a mechanism, diagram, map or landscape, either in response to questioning or as a way of requesting further information.

PROGRAMME EVALUATION

The two formal terms you will come across frequently are formative evaluation and summative evaluation. In essence, these two differ from each other in purpose and timing.

Formative Evaluations

A formative evaluation is conducted in order to provide feedback to the design or refinement process. Its purpose is to enable changes to be made before the work is finalized.

In practice a formative evaluation rarely looks at fundamental issues of programme effectiveness. The reason for this is simple: by the time enough data has been assembled to make the evaluation meaningful, there is usually too much invested in a programme in the way of time and effort to allow for a fundamental redesign of the work which has been done.

Instead, formative evaluations usually seek to acquire feedback on a less drastic scale so that the program can be improved rather than completely changed or scrapped. This feedback is obtained by a study of user reactions, observation of the programmes in use with sample target users, questionnaires, assessments of test scores, and so on.

Summative Evaluations

A summative evaluation is conducted after the program has been finished. Its purpose is retrospective: to determine whether the completed courseware has met the design criteria.

Once your programme has been designed, implemented and trialled an evaluation will almost certainly be required. It is obviously a matter of some importance to determine whether the program does what is intended.

You may wish to conduct a quantitative or a qualitative evaluation. In a qualitative evaluation, you will try to establish the users' feelings and reactions to the program. You will wish to assess user perceptions about things such as ease of use, instructional value and benefit, motivation and so on. The things which a qualitative evaluation attempts to determine are subjective, and you will probably wish to use questionnaires to conduct them.

For an example of an evaluation questionnaire designed to establish user attitudes, see the questionnaire quoted later in this chapter.(pp 132-133)

In a quantitative evaluation you will seek to measure the programme's effect. The issues you will consider and the assessment tools you may use in making these measurements include:

(a) Are the teaching objectives met? Post Tests to establish mastery.

(b) Is the learning retained over time? Follow-up tests after a specified period.

(c) Does the IV courseware compare favourably in effectiveness to other (maybe cheaper) forms of training? Comparison of test scores as against scores obtained by control groups taught by conventional means.

(d) Does the IV courseware compare favourably in terms of training time required for mastery as opposed to other methods. As above, comparison between test group and control group.

However, it is important to remember that we are dealing with a medium which is said to offer a great deal that is new and which is certainly extremely expensive and difficult to implement. There are, therefore, other questions that should always be asked in assessing the success of an IV program.

(a) Does it provide new learning opportunities not available from other media?

(b) Does it do something necessary which can be done in no other way?

CASE STUDY: THE NORTH WEST EDUCATIONAL COMPUTING PROJECT

Background

The North West Educational Computing Project (NWECP) was not strictly a training but an educational project. However, many of the lessons learned and the methodologies which were evolved (both in terms of learning and design) have equal relevance to the training field.

The following is an account of the design process which went into the creation of the courseware, including a discussion of the reasons which led to design decisions and revisions.

The NWECP was originated at Lancashire Polytechnic and funded by IBM United Kingdom Trust and Lancashire Polytechnic with support from the University of Manchester.

The IBM PC in Schools Project functioned from September 1984 in 11 European countries. Its aims were to further education for the information society, to promote involvement by teachers and students of all ages, to facilitate assessment of hardware and software, to encourage the development of new materials and to stimulate change across the curriculum.

The aims of NWECP were very broad and general: the team was asked to 'investigate the potential of interactive video for foreign language learning'.

Foreign language learning was chosen as an applications area for a number of reasons. First, foreign languages was identified as an area of the curriculum notably lacking in quality software. Second, the ability of IV to supply high quality audio and visuals seemed to offer the possibility of designing courseware more in keeping with modern communicative methods for language teaching than conventional computer-aided learning was generally able to provide. In support of the proposal IBM assigned an educatic nal relations adviser with a background in language training to work closely witl the project.

Timescale

The team benefited from a more generous development period than is usual in commercial IV development. The period of time often quoted for the implementation and delivery of a commercial IV package is usually between four and six months. In the case of the NWECP, the actual design, development and implementation phase of the project ran for 14 months after an initial training, information gathering and feasibility phase lasting just over a year.

Target Groups
The target groups were foreign language learners in secondary schools, considered to be an extremely difficult target.

Objectives
The content design team set themselves a deceptively simple overall objective which soon proved to represent a difficult task. It was determined that the IV courseware produced by the project should be capable of actually teaching spoken foreign language.

To clarify this objective further, let us define it as follows: the team wished learners to be able to come to the IV workstation, to switch on the system and to work through a programme and to be able to leave the workstation with the ability to understand, speak and use appropriately foreign language phrases which were previously unknown.

The team soon realized that this objective, to the best of their knowledge after an exhaustive information-gathering exercise, had not been met by any existing CBT or IV package.

It is now generally recognized that traditional grammar-translation methods of language teaching cannot properly teach spoken foreign language. Generations of British language learners testify to the fact that traditional qualifications in foreign language obtainable in the UK have certificated the ability to write the foreign language but not to speak it.

In order to teach spoken language, the spoken word is required as stimulus and model. Existing CBT packages cannot provide the spoken word; hence the small amount of CBT software available in this area and the fact that what is available tends to be dry grammatical or vocabulary exercises.

Simulations are the other main type of software available for language learning. These are usually of the adventure game format, create a (hopefully) authentic foreign language environment and require users to make decisions and find their way through while meeting various objectives. Indeed, this kind of simulation seems to be the natural thought of language specialist and layman alike when considering the appropriateness of CBT techniques to language learning.

The problem faced by the design team was this: neither of the principal types of CBT courseware in the subject area - drill and practice or simulations - was actually capable of teaching foreign languages. Normal user input procedures as discussed earlier were simply not suitable for language learning — in order to learn a language, one must speak language and the days of speech recognition by computers at an appropriate level for foreign language learning are still many years away.

Existing language courseware does not teach language; it provides drill, practice, follow-up and exploitation work of language which has been taught and learned in some other place and in some other way, generally in the languages classroom.

Computers are good at setting up problem solving activities; they are good at text and number processing and analysis. However, none of these things are remotely connected with the language acquisition stage of foreign language learning, which is not a problem-solving or decision-making activity.

Traditional ways of using CBT were, therefore, deemed to be inappropriate for the objectives of the project. Furthermore, it was soon found that published work and the general view of IV as a medium also offered very little that was useful.

In brief, there were, it seemed, two well understood approaches to IV design for education and training. One could crudely be described as the 'pictorial database' approach — using the videodisc as a repository of a large quantity of photographic still frames to be used as an information resource to be accessed in a number of ways. The other was the branching simulation type of programme in which the aim of the designer is to provide differentiated video feedback to learner decisions.

Once again, neither of these design approaches came remotely close to offering the possibility of a system which could actually teach spoken language. The simulation approach, which is the one generally used in IV for foreign language tuition, is capable of providing practice of language which has been learned in a more conventional way, and the still frame database approach cannot show authentic behaviour as a model for study.

It was at this stage of impasse that it became necessary to abandon both these approaches in order to produce materials which could actually teach spoken language.

We will stress here how important this decision was and how it helped to forge the whole design philosophy of the project. It was a conscious decision that IV was to be used to fulfil an educational task in the way best suited to providing a successful and appropriate educational solution. Many IV teams have a fixed view of what IV courseware is and can do, and the educational or training objective is often distorted to fit conventional concepts of the medium.

The Two Templates

Template 1

Courseware development on this project naturally fell into two main segments resulting in two major courseware packages which were known to the project team as Templates 1 and 2.

Template 1 employed off-the-shelf videodisc material and took the form of relatively structured language acquisition programmes.

Following the completion of Template 1 and its installation in project schools, its use was evaluated. The feedback from this evaluation and the lessons which had emerged during the design phase, were fed into the design of the programmes of Template 2. This process enabled the team to incorporate in the final programmes the specific IV lessons which emerged from the evaluation study.

(a) The Video Resource

The video resource required was a number of dialogues in the target language. The project team was extremely fortunate in being able to locate and use for experimental purposes an off-the-shelf videodisc produced by the BBC, the videodisc version of the Ensemble French teaching cassette tape and broadcast TV programme intended for adult leaners.

Although the dialogues themselves were rather dated and mannered in their delivery style, and although a number of difficulties were experienced because of the essentially linear nature of the original material, the 24 dialogues on the Ensemble videodiscs were an invaluable resource.

(b) The Programmes
The learner's path through the programme is as follows.

(1) Entry

There are three ways of entering programmes: direction to dialogue 1 for the first time user, answering questions in a pre-test for those requiring guidance and learner choice.

The opening screen asks if the user has used the programmes before. If the answer is no, the user is directed to insert disc 1 side 1, and lesson 1 is automatically loaded.

If the learner asks for the pretest, the English language version of a statement from dialogue 1 is shown on screen. The learner is asked 'Can you say this in French?' Pressing the space bar reveals the correct version (in text) in French on the screen, and the learner is asked if his/her answer was correct. If the learner does not know the answer, it is presumed that the language of dialogue 1 has not been mastered, and dialogue 1 is therefore selected. If the answer is correct, the process is repeated for each dialogue until a question is encountered which cannot be answered. At that point, the appropriate dialogue is selected.

The user may choose a dialogue by number, and may also enter the learning sequence at any one of its principal stages.

(2) The Learning Sequence

Step 1 Imitation
As a first introduction to the dialogue to be studied, the whole video and audio sequence is played through without interruption and with no overlaid text on screen.

At the end of this unpaused sequence, the learner may continue into the learning sequence or review the video.

The Step 1 exercise
Each dialogue is divided into utterances of suitable length. The video and audio play to the end of the utterance and go into still frame. As the on-screen character speaks, a subtitle in the target language appears on screen, remains for as long as it took to speak the utterance and is then erased. The learner imitates the foreign language utterance. With the first imitation cue the learner is given the meaning of the utterance in English in a subtitle which appears after the French subtitle as is then also erased, and thereafter this English refresher is given every fourth repetition.

Learners may decide for themselves how often to repeat a particular utterance and when to move on to the next.

It is also possible to step backwards one utterance at a time, so that the user is never controlled by the software. Exit from the programme is always possible simply by pressing the escape key.

Step 2 Interpretation

At the end of step 1, users may exit or continue to step 2. At the start of step 2, it is possible to see the whole unbroken sequence again before starting the interpretation exercise.

The cue given is the English utterance with the silenced video segment: the learner is required to speak the French equivalent. Pressing a specified key gives the segment again with audio, and pressing another gives the segment with audio and French text. Once again, the number of repetitions is left entirely to the user and it is possible to step backwards and to exit at any time.

Step 3 Substitution and Extension

The elements of language acquired in Steps 1 and 2 are permutated to give many variations, and are extended to produce longer utterances. Once again the cue is in English and the learner is required to respond in the foreign language.

The drill in step 3 is based on substitution tables constructed from the elements of language taught in Steps 1 and 2 and in previous dialogues. Elements of language which have previously been taught are used to form many different utterances in order to extend the possibilities of the language and structures contained in the dialogues.

It is estimated that the present Step 3 tables can display more than 100 000 separate cues and responses.

(c) The Evaluation

It was decided to aim the evaluation questionnaire at establishing the attitudes of users and teachers to the system, their perception of the benefits (or otherwise) of the system and their views as expressed in discussion. In addition, learners of varying types and levels were observed as they used the system and feedback from teachers was sought at follow-up workshops and meetings.

The evaluation was dual purpose in another way: it was both summative of the completed Template 1 programmes and formative for the Template 2 programmes to come.

The Evaluation Questionnaire

The questionnaire was administered to groups of users after they had been observed using the system. As well as noting the specific answers to questions, any fuller answers were recorded and written up as part of the evaluation report.

We list here the questions which were asked, as an example of the sort of things we wished to know: in every case the users were asked to respond on a scale of 1-5, corresponding to the following reactions:

1   Very difficult/Strongly disagree
2   Difficult/Disagree
3   Average/No opinion
4   Easy/Agree
5   Very easy/Strongly agree

Questionnaire

Have you used the interactive video system before?

How easy or difficult do you find it to use the programmes?

> Getting into the programme
> Understanding what to do
> Finding your way round
> Using the keys to control the programme
> Keeping track of where you are
> Getting out of the programme

What are your views on the following?

> I enjoy using the system
> It helps me learn French
> It helps me speak French
> It helps me understand spoken French
> It helps me read French
> It helps me understand written French
> The work is easy
> I use the things I learn in
> > French lessons
> > French homework
> > French tests/exams

When using the system,compared to French lessons I
> work harder
> work faster
> speak more French
> spend more time getting it right
> do work I don't normally do

The advantages of the system are:

> I can choose a dialogue
> The dialogues are
> > well acted
> > interesting
> > funny
> The language is useful
> The actors are native speakers
> I can speak as many times as I like
> I can move around the programme

I can repeat without embarrassment
I can see peoples' expressions
I can see peoples' movements
I can see peoples' lips move
I can do lots of practice
I am in charge of my own learning

What improvements or changes would you like to see?

What other features would you like to see included?
        to make the programmes easier to use
        to improve your learning
Which part of the programmes do you like best?
Which part of the programmes do you like least?

Results of the Evaluation
It became clear very early on that the most successful element of the programmes for the users was the learner choice and control built into the learning process. Even though the methodology which had been employed was fairly structured, the choice factors built into the design enabled a large degree of learner independence which was greeted with enormous enthusiasm. Effectively, a large number of the users (ranging in age from 11 to 16) felt that they had responsibility for their own learning and could exercise choice in respect of which type of language to study and issues of pace, thoroughness and work rate.

Furthermore, many users were observed using choices which had been provided in ways which had not been anticipated by the project team. Many users, for instance, felt it beneficial to work through Step 2 twice as a matter of course. Some less motivated and less able pupils were observed using the programmes as a resource for comprehension rather than intensive spoken work, and the ability of the IV programmes to remotivate these pupils was considered significant by the school.

Some other evidence also began to show through by the end of the evaluation period: in one project school, pupils began to arrive at school more than one hour before the start of school in order to make voluntary use of the system, and in the same school the take-up rate of a (voluntary) second foreign language amongst a group making intensive use of the system increased by 200 per cent.

Template 2
Even during the design process of Template 1, the project team was beginning to feel that much more could be done. To these feelings were added the findings of the evaluation, and the whole was merged to form a background to the design of the second major segment of the project's work.
(a) The Video Material
Initially this feeling sprang from the nature of the video and language contained on the Ensemble discs. Because these materials had been produced for linear viewing, the acting style was rather mannered and artificially slow, and the editing of the original tape material threw up many problems when the disc was subjected to the

segmentation and freeze-frame techniques required by the instructional design.

The speed and style of language were particularly important. Because the software was able to exploit very efficiently the ability of the videodisc to display very short sequences with pin-point accuracy, there was felt to be no need to use artificially slow language delivery: when you can display and repeat a segment on screen instantaneously and at will, it becomes possible and preferable to study authentic language spoken at natural speed. One independent academic likened the effect of the programmes to that of the naturalist's hide, which permits the observer to view and study perfect snapshots of natural behaviour in an authentic context.

In order for this analogy to be valid, however, it is necessary to have examples of natural behaviour available on videodisc , and in our case this meant examples of natural language behaviour. For our purposes there was a huge gulf between the staged language of professional actors and the natural language of amateurs.

This is not to say that the amateurs were better actors than the professionals: far from it. The professional actors are generally more convincing and always less wooden than amateurs in an unbroken video viewing. However, when it came to segmenting their speeches into small chunks and freeze-framing at expressive moments, we almost invariably found that the very lack of professional control over facial expression and gesture led to a far more powerful and useful visual message coming from the still frames to support the meaning of the language being uttered.

(b) The Design

The second main area of revision was that made desirable by user reactions to Template 1 programmes. As outlined above, the pupils were observed making unexpected use of those choices which were built into the structured language acquisition exercises. It was in response to these observations that the design choices were made which, in the opinion of the team, resulted in programmes which were a truly IV solution to a teaching requirement.

On analysing these unexpected choices the design team became aware that none of them were, in fact, harmful. It was realized, that the free choices which were available were allowing enterprising students to assemble, to some extent, their own preferred learning strategy.

We had, at this point, two clear choices. One was to redesign the courseware to make it more rigid and to impose the learning structure more forcibly upon the learners. The other was to use the feedback to increase those aspects of user control to allow and encourage learners to assemble their own learning strategy, and to assume as much autonomy and responsibility as possible in the learning process.

The general design philosophy which was adopted was to allow as many non-harmful options as possible to the users. Obviously some judgment was necessary in the design process: it was necessary, for example, to exclude activities which had been proved by research to be harmful to the language learning process. Beyond this we felt, and still feel, that one of the chief benefits of the IV medium is its ability to allow for a difference in preferred learning styles.

(c) The Dialogues

Dialogues were shot using amateur actors on location in schools in France and Germany. Brief scenarios were drawn up by members of the project team and sent to contact schools where dialogues were scripted and acted mostly by young people in the same age range as the target learners. In the course of this filming it was necessary to adopt some quite unconventional strategies to overcome the time constraints and the inexperience of the amateur actors. In all, 12 French and 13 German dialogues were shot.

The language on the videodiscs is spoken at natural speed, exploiting to a much greater extent the flexibility and responsiveness of the developed software.

(d) The Courseware

(1) Entry

There is no attempt to direct users to a particular dialogue: they are first asked to select whether they wish to work in French or German and are then free to choose any dialogue or activity. The three choices from the main menu are Viewing, Printing and Activities.

(2) Viewing

In Template 2, learners are offered the facility to view the dialogues in a variety of ways — paused or unpaused, with or without sound, with foreign language subtitles, with English language subtitles, with both or with neither. In all, there are 16 possible ways to view each dialogue.

It is possible, therefore, to choose an unpaused viewing with sound but no subtitles in order to view the dialogue straight through. Unlike Template 1 this choice is not imposed on the learner.

To work intensively with the dialogue, learners would choose a paused viewing, perhaps with sound and with foreign language subtitles.

In a paused dialogue, the utterances are longer and faster than in Template 1, reflecting the more natural language employed in the dialogues. More highly developed software has however improved access times, so that utterances can be recalled instantaneously. Subtitling is erased before learners imitate the utterance, thereby preventing interference from the text. Available keys allow users to repeat; continue to the next utterance; return to the previous utterance; repeat the current utterance with the opposite choice of subtitles; and toggle sound on or off.

For this option as for all others, the keys are chosen to fall easily under the hands by touch so that the learner's attention is not distracted from the screen. The use of the keyboard is considered more practical than a touch screen for this application in view of the intensive interaction involved. The remainder of the keyboard (ie all keys which are not 'live') is disabled, so that the only method of leaving the programme is to press <Escape> which is available at all times. This robustness was considered essential for school use, but is also extremely comforting to adult users.

More recent work has used a mouse as the input device in order to reduce still further any barrier to the user's completely free control of the courseware.

(3) Printing

A printing menu allows learners to print either the whole of a dialogue or each individual role separately. This print can be used for follow-up activities away from the workstation. It has also been found motivating for users to be able to take some tangible material away from a session.

(4) Activities

Finally there is the activities menu which offers learners a range of activities with the dialogues. Learners or teachers can browse across the whole surface of the disc, employing most of the facilities of the videodisc player.

The most important learning option is the role-play. In this option, learners or groups of learners have the facility, having first had the opportunity to learn the language in the dialogue, to view each character in the chosen dialogue, to select one, and to engage in a role-play with characters on the videodisc.

Support available includes the ability to reveal the subtitle one word at a time, to view the silenced utterance or to repeat the utterance with or without sound an unlimited number of times.

There are also games designed to focus the attention of learners on non-verbal and paralinguistic clues in the communicative process, such as surroundings, body-language, facial expressions and so on. These games involve matching silent video sequences to one audio clip, or audio clips to one silent video sequence.

Chapter 5

SOFTWARE

INTRODUCTION

As with any computer based system, the quality of an IV system's performance lies in the quality of its software. The driving force within an IV system is the computer program. Whether you approach IV through video, instructional design or computing is irrelevant; the quality of the system is reflected in the quality of its software.

The features of IV should be fully exploited to give the user a unique experience they could not have from any other medium. Any full scale IV project or package will involve complex software running into thousands of lines of code. It is common in IV to see snippets of what could be done. However, look to a completed project or package to gauge just what is involved in the production of a working system. Developing software for IV is a non-trivial task.

A novice to IV will more than likely be impressed by almost any working system. After all, it is the most powerful audiovisual tool available, and presented in such a controlled manner, which hitherto was not possible, will always provide a favourable impression. However, compared to the possibilities the medium offers, the majority of available IV packages do not utilize the unique capabilities of the medium and consequently cannot provide that totally new learning experience which IV promises. In the last analysis it is the software which translates the ideas into an implemented system. The most prominent reason for failure in IV is the lack of quality of software. This is partly due to the originality of the medium as vendors rush the market with software, irrespective of its performance. Another major reason is in the nature of the medium, in that knowledge from a range of disciplines has to be fused.

Throughout this book we have reinforced the fact that quality IV is a result of the convergence of various skills. Much emphasis is placed on the quality of the video images, and rightly so, much emphasis is placed on the instructional design, and rightly so. Then, almost as an afterthought, the design is handed to an author or programmer who is expected correctly to implement the design ideas provided by instructional and subject experts. In many cases instructional designers believe themselves capable of implementing a software system. This is the most disastrous of routes. More than any other facet of the system, the software expert must be a perfectionist. Extra demands are also made on the programmer since, not only does he or she need to be a specialist in their own topic, they must tolerate and accommodate the intrusion of other experts into their domain. This is not a devaluation of the role of software; rather it is further acknowledgement of the crucial role software plays in IV.

Motivation is gained or lost through a user's interaction with the system, usually focused on the screen. Whilst there are obvious implications for the quality of design of the content material, the crucial part is at the point of delivery. It really doesn't matter how good the the material presented to the learner is if the vehicle on which it is delivered has inadequate performance levels.

There is no shortage of ideas in IV. An entire book could have been written on the development of IV software. The following sections of this chapter serve to introduce topics and are not intended as an extensive review of the software development process.

What is Software?

The term 'software' is usually used as a synonym for computer programs and *vice versa*. Most professionals in the IV business and a substantial proportion of the general public, could hazard a reasonable guess as to what software actually means. But would they be correct? A simple textbook definition might be: 'software is the sets of instructions that when executed control the computer (hardware) in order to perform some desired function'. There is no doubt that other, more complete definitions could be offered, but a comprehensive definition is not as important as understanding the characteristics of software and its role in the complex environment of IV.

Software, as distinct from hardware, is not manufactured in a classical sense but is developed or engineered. The manufacture of a computer is a direct transcription of the design drawings into the physical form. Software is fundamentally a logical system, engineered in order to control the computer and any peripherals such as a videodisc player. Producing software is a highly labour intensive operation , even with computer-aided tools, and is therefore more of a craft. Hardware and software do have some similarities in that quality is achieved by good design and both are dependant on skilled people in the delivery of the final product.

The physical set-up of an IV system is a mixture of different technologies which allows for the application of any training situation, however complex, in a cost effective and beneficial way. The development of software, whether programmed or authored, is a complex and difficult job. In most cases it is the software rather than the hardware which differentiates quality products in IV. However, compared to the speed of technological progress in hardware, the evolution of the software culture has been painfully slow. As such, software has become a limiting factor in the application of existing hardware technology.

Software Problems

The invention of the microcomputer greatly increased the quantity of computer software available to people from backgrounds which had previously little or no experience of computers and software. Small computers which are capable of mainframe performance but with very few software development facilities were now available at a relatively cheap price. This availability of raw computing power had the inevitable side-effect of the growth in amateur programming. This in turn has had an adverse effect on the development of theories, methods, skills and tools used to produce software, known as software engineering.

Current software problems for IV fall into two categories. There are questions to be asked about available software and there are issues to be addressed about potential software.

There is a distinct lack of quality software in most IV applications presently on the market. The overall conclusion is that IV software has suffered in quality for one of two reasons:

(1) Subject experts could possibly devise educationally sound programmes, but for various reasons - lack of funds, lack of effective communications with the computer programmer, programs written by the subject specialist - the resulting computer implementation greatly diluted the original educational intentions.

(2) Computer specialists with no or little subject expertise produced computer programs of quality but which were educationally unsound.

The inter-disciplinary nature of an IV project will usually mean that at least some members of the project team should feel comfortable in computing surroundings and understand the limitations of the technology. A positive advantage of this is the orientation of non-specialists towards computing . A major negative effect is when this leads to amateur programming, with non-specialists perceiving themselves as competent in the computing field.

The phrase 'software crisis' is used to refer to a set of problems encountered in the development of computer software in all application areas, including IV. Also, the problems are not restricted to software which 'doesn't work properly'. Problems often begin at the analytical or user requirements stage, and are then successively compounded through the design, coding and testing stages. The term 'coding' is often used as a synonym for programming by computer professionals. Too often the failure of a project has been caused by 'we're running out of time, we'd better get down to coding'.

For proposed software projects, these problems have to be avoided. One certain fact is that indulging in amateur programming for an IV system is asking for trouble. But, amateur programming aside, there are still serious problems which apply to the development of quality software in the IV environment:

(1) Project managers or team leaders who have a limited grasp of software issues yet affect the process of software development.

(2) Software development is often taken as an afterthought, with no real planning or timetabling.

(3) Issues of software development begin with the bottom line issues of cost and productivity rather than the quality issues of analysis and design.

(4) There is a skills shortage in software expertise in the IV field.

(5) It is difficult to accurately estimate software timescales and costs.

(6) Most programmers do not have an education or training in software engineering.

The above is a brief synopsis for which the only solution is an engineering approach to software development. This, coupled with experience and an improvement of techniques and tools within IV, is the key to better software. Of course this is easier said than done especially since IV is a relatively new medium and developers will not readily share their expertise. However the one fact remains that as systems become more sophisticated, software will absorb a growing percentage of the overall development costs. The problems of software development have to be taken seriously.

Software Engineering

The previous section laid out the bad news. The good news will hopefully solve all or at least most of the above problems —software engineering. Although problems of software development will not disappear overnight, recognizing that problems exist is the first step toward a solution. The main problem concerning IV is that present day authoring techniques cannot tap the full potential offered by available technology, and with continual development of hardware the problem will become more acute.

Software engineering is the application of science and mathematics to the development of software. This collection of theories, methods, skills and tools, blended with experience, produce quality software. Although still in its infancy when compared to other engineering disciplines, the techniques of software engineering are suitable for the complex arena of IV where, generally, there will be people from varying backgrounds involved in the project. The term 'software engineering' is really an all- embracing term for the production of quality software.

This book is not about software engineering, but this chapter does try to reflect the principles of the discipline as it applies to IV. This is especially true of the case study at the end of the chapter where the techniques were used to the benefit of the project outlined in the case study. For anyone who is to undertake or supervise software development in an IV project they are recommended to consult textbooks on the subject of software engineering and familiarize themselves with the stages of software development and the techniques used. Throughout this section the terms 'software designer' and 'software developer' are taken to be synonyms for a software engineer.

COMPREHENSION

It is inevitable, at least in the earlier stages of an IV project, that communications will bring some problems. It is to be expected that experts from varying fields will bring their own jargon and knowledge into a situation where others will it find difficult to follow. Problems in developing quality software not only stem from its inherent complexity as a process, but also from the inevitable lack of comprehension between the specialist strands of the project.

There are three clearly identifiable areas in IV where communication problems may hamper progress:

(1) Project staff from different backgrounds working together as a team.
(2) A management or supervisory body who have little or no knowledge of IV.
(3) Software practitioners in the field of IV who are amateur programmers give a biased and inaccurate account of software development to other members of the team.

Communication skills and interpersonal skills play a crucial role throughout the project. At least the subject expert and/or the instructional designer and the software engineer should have a sufficient depth of knowledge in their own area to provide sensible paradigms. This understanding is particularly important because it enables the transfer of ideas into a coherent and unambiguous specification.

When software is discussed in IV circles, there is a tendency to generalize about particular systems or authoring languages. This is understandable to some extent. However, when these generalities are expanded to influence a software decision misconceptions can arise. Detail becomes very important when software is to be developed for IV and a variety of similes and analogies to account for particular characteristics of a computer program can be very misleading.

The communications process developed within a project will have an influential effect on software design. It is of paramount importance that the project team is a team. In our experience, one of the fundamental necessities for a successful project is the evolution of a dialogue between the team members, and the quality of interpersonal skills which is implicit.

User Requirements Specification

The user requirements specification is an extremely important document and identifies the general scope of the system. This is an irreplaceable part of software development which, as the name suggests, involves the users and/or instructional designers. The URS should be viewed as the stage where detailed requirements are assimilated and analysed, usually in plain English, from potential users or clients. It should be a joint venture with the involved parties. A URS is not a document which forms the basis for the computer programming. Rather it will be the source document for a fuller software specification, which will then form the basic blueprint for implementation. At this stage it might not be the software specialist who writes this document. It is not uncommon for instructional designers to be the focal point for this stage. Regardless of who actually pens the URS, the overall aim of the document is a legible, detailed specification which is, as far as possible, free of errors, ambiguity, redundancy, duplication and contradiction.

Ideally the URS will evolve from a series of meetings between the involved project team and certainly the users or customers. However, it may be that only the software designer fully understands the purpose of such a document. Therefore, the software designer should be armed with questions that help the participants describe their requirements in a clear and concise fashion.

Users are not interested in how a computer actually does things; they are far more interested in what it does and how they interact with it. Input and output are the key factors in developing an IV software system. What is required from a URS falls into four areas:
-   output requirements (system to user)
-   input requirements (user to system)
-   operational detail
-   system constraints.

The initial set of questions focus on output and typical questions might be: -
- Who is to receive the output?
- What is the output to achieve?
- What information is to be output?
- What is the output device?
- In what form - graphical? videodisc? words?
- What is the content of the output?
- Is the output to be in answer form or help?
- How is the output regulated or monitored?

These questions can of course be expanded upon or customized and probably more questions will be added for specific systems. This initial set of questions will generally provide the software engineer with a grasp of the overall system objectives.

The second set of questions focus on the input, with possible questions being:
- What device is to be used for input?
- What form will the input take?
- What type of information is acceptable?
- Is input in answer form or part of a dialogue?
- How is the input to be validated?
- Is it solely the user who provides input?
- How is input to be prompted for?
- Is there a standard layout for input?

Like the output questions, these will be refined and customized as necessary. At this stage there should be a string of loosely related answers. However, there will be a substantial amount of information on how the system will function.

After the output and input questions comes the stage of trying to ascertain the overall operation of the system in some detail.

This part is less 'mechanical' in that it is not really a question and answer session, but more of a 'conversation' session. At this point there needs to be an understanding of the users' perception of how the system will function. The answers to the output and input questions have to be expanded on in the light the overall presentation.

Clarification of the function of the system should be sought in terms of the relationship between the input and output. This usually leads to how the customers perceive the manipulation of the information within the computer. Attention should be paid to all remarks made at this stage since usually, after detailing the output and input, the discussion will centre around the system as a whole. Experience has suggested that this is where customers perceive the role of video, graphics and text in the overall package. The main consideration at this stage is never to force words out of the participants — they should feel comfortable enough to say almost anything without the fear of an indignant reply!

Last, but not least, the constraints of the system have to be ascertained. There are many reasons why the URS could be restricted and at least the following issues must be explored:

- Are there technical restrictions?
- Are there human resource restrictions?
- Are there constraints due to the environment?
- Is there a minimum performance level?
- How is the finance organised?

The first question in this list is very vague and could be expanded to include everything from the use of colours on screen to the number of buttons on a mouse. With the multitude of IV hardware components on the market, the ideal is to have the freedom to construct a hardware system that will complement the software to deliver the optimal system for the user requirements.

Arriving at a URS will probably not be done at one meeting. The usual course is for the specification to be drafted, and then revised and refined until customers are satisfied that it is a clear reflection of their requirements.

Functional Specification

When the URS exists, the first view of the system is completed. As such, this specification is not of sufficient structure and clarity to form the basis for software design. There has to be a stage between user requirements and design in order to completely eliminate ambiguity, duplication, redundancy and also clarify intent and correct any omissions. In the jargon jungle of IV terminology there is great scope for misinformation and misinterpretation.

The functional specification expresses the requirements in a concise and accurate form, which is understandable to both users and the implementers. It also provides a measurement for estimating timescale (and therefore cost), software design, quality assurance and is also a yardstick for measuring progress at review meetings. It is usual that the software designer should develop this specification, but not in isolation. There will necessarily be communications with all the project team and the users in order to reach agreement.

The necessity for this document stems from the inherent instability of the URS which will, typically, have to go through an iterative loop of clarification and refinement in its transformation to a functional specification.

Two of the primary reasons for the unstable nature of a URS from a software point of view are vagueness and the informal, and therefore unstructured, nature of additions. Use of words such as 'maybe', 'should', and 'perhaps' are examples that often cloud the actual intention. However well intended, a URS will usually need to be clarified. The other problem with a URS is the 'afterthought syndrome'. This could be a major problem area. Because IV is still in its infancy, new ideas emerge throughout the specification stage. The tendency is then to tag on these ideas thus making partitioning of the system into appropriate categories more unstructured than it need be. The solution is to have extensive and wide ranging discussions with the users.

As with the URS the functional scope of the system is specific to the application in question. However this functional analysis of the system, laid out in natural language terms, will also contain the hardware specification as well as a more precise description of the system requirements.

The main parts of the functional blueprint are the inputs, operations and outputs. A coherent specification will show a trace from the inputs through the operations to the outputs. The following is a minimum checklist for the functional specification and will probably be added to and customised according to the situation:

Input
- medium (eg touch screen, keyboard, mouse)
- initiator (person, internal, other)
- entry to system (choice, controlled)
- format (eg. one-touch, free form)
- interrupts (on/off, specific key)
- location (eg unrestricted, specified)
- errors (eg time-out, wrong keys)

Operations
- hardware specification
- portability (software, hardware)
- specific system features such as:
>   videodisc (eg use, amount, control)
>   graphics (eg use, generation, mix)
>   screen layout (content, format)
>   answer processing
>   answer feedback
>   answer recording
>   mathematical computations
>   statistical records
- authorised access
- data security (eg files, records)
- acceptable minimal input
- response time
- exception handling (eg unexpected key)

Output
- medium (eg screen, printer)
- recipient (eg person, internal file)
- aim of (eg reinforcement, feedback)
- form (eg video, graphics, text, mix)
- message/error box

The above list basically contains headings which have to be more clearly defined and expanded - this could be a fairly lengthy document. However the time spent on correctly specifying an IV system will return itself in terms of quality and a great reduction in error correction in the later stages of software development.

IV Software Lifecycle

There is no adequate method, short of complex and elaborate diagrams, of expressing the generic activities within the software engineering process. What is clear is that the development of software is not a linear but a cyclic process. The cycle is not a formula but a visual representation of the development path. It provides non-technical people with an understanding of the nature of the development process. In essence it makes the software development process visible and comprehensible to all parties involved in the project.

Figure 1 shows an actual example which was used in the project outlined in the case study at the end of this chapter. Although used for a specific project it displays the important stages of any software package developed for IV.

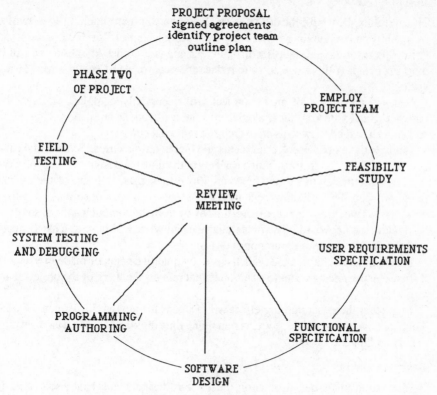

Figure 1 Project Lifecycle

DESIGNING THE SYSTEM

Designing the system is perhaps the most important part of the software development process. The overall goal of the design stage is to produce a model of a solution to the functional requirements which can easily be transcribed into a computer program.

At this point there exists an unambiguous functional specification, written in

English, which is agreed and understood by all parties involved in the project. The vitally important task of designing the software solution can now be undertaken. The importance of design cannot be overstated. No-one would consider building a house without professionally constructed plans, yet many people embark on computer programming with scant regard for design and quality.

Many would-be computer programmers believe that the sooner you begin tapping the keyboard, the sooner you will have a completed program. However the task is not so much in getting the program to work, but rather in getting the program right. The difference between getting a program to work and getting it right is basically the difference between the amateur and the professional.

Design Philosophy

The overall objective for the design of an IV software system should be to minimize complexity and put maximum flexibility under learner control. This is easier said than done. Good software design is a difficult task and takes time. Attention to detail is most important at this stage so as to reduce the occurrence of costly errors during testing.

Because the nature of an IV project will necessarily combine, at least, the computing and videodisc technologies plus the applications area, the design of the software should be viewed as an exercise in reducing complexity.

Properly developed user requirements and functional specifications will make the task of designing the software much easier. By the time the design stage of software development arrives there may be some 30 - 40 per cent, at least, of the overall timescale spent. This will have been time well spent. A competent software engineer will spend as much, and perhaps more, time away from the computer as he or she does working at the keyboard. The preparatory design work will pose at least as many problems as the actual programming.

Programming is either made much easier by quality design, or made much more difficult by poor design, and to a certain extent reflects the work of the project team as a whole.

In general the programming effort will account for around 30 per cent of total software development time, with the remaining time divided between design, testing and debugging the system.

Design principles

Before setting out the design notation, the software designer must have a set of criteria which must be applied consistently. Software design is at the heart of software engineering. Without it there is great difficulty in translating the requirements into an operational system. At this stage the system is further developed to make the best use of the available computing and video resources. From detailed design a software system is developed to tap the full potential of the hardware.

The process of design is completed in three stages:

    (1) The type of data and its structure which is to be processed within the program is defined

    (2) The system is broken down into appropriate modules in a hierarchical fashion

(3)   The modules are then detailed in a manner which facilitates transcription to computer code.

Step one entails looking at the data which is to be input by the user, manipulated by the computer and output to the output device. It is very important that data can be manipulated in the most effective way. Strings of characters are commonplace in an IV system so it is important that the structures, including external text or binary files, are designed properly. Operations on strings can be cumbersome and slow if the initial structure is wrongly constructed.

The second stage involves partitioning the system into modules, or environments. These modules are further decomposed until they are of manageable size and easily coded. A module is an expression of a section of code, or procedure, which perform a certain task. In order to provide for maximum control and flexibility, the design of the software must be highly structured. The developed technique which best represents this stage of design is that of 'stepwise refinement', also commonly referred to as 'top-down' design. Stepwise refinement successively breaks down the modules so that each module is of lesser complexity than the one preceding it (higher than it).

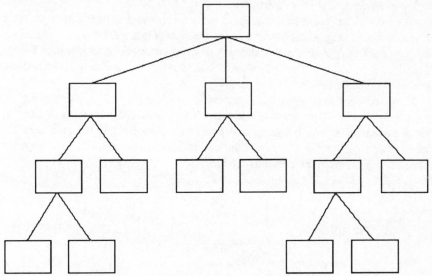

Figure 2 Hierarchical tree

There are two main influences on this 'tree-like' structure (see Figure two). First, the user and functional specifications may evolve natural divisions that map well on to design. Another impact will be the construction of the data structures since they will form part or all of the information passing between modules.

Good design ensuring efficient code also helps maintainability. Both these aims are achieved if the design is highly cohesive and loosely coupled. A high degree of cohesion is exhibited when all the operations within a module relate to the actual function of the module, an example being an answer analysis module. Operations grouped together for other reasons, such as to perform actions at a given time irrespective of their function, will have a low degree of cohesion. Coupling indicates the interconnection between modules and is related to cohesion. Loosely coupled systems have modules which are independent or almost independent program units, that is, they are highly cohesive. Highly coupled systems involve strong interconnections where program units are dependant on other modules. Highly cohesive and loosely coupled systems make detailed design understandable and ensure that any changes will be local to a single module.

The third stage involves the detailed design of each module. The process is an iterative one in that the system is continually refined and detailed. The modules are now of a manageable size and can now be detailed in the 'lowest-level' of detail prior to coding. Irrespective of the intricacies of the authoring or programming language a design notation should be used which transcends coding peculiarities.

The Design Notation

A consistent design notation throughout a project, and indeed between projects, is immensely valuable. Apart from consistency advantages, it also allows testing and evaluation to be thoroughly carried out.

This notation can either be in chart or diagram form or as an actual 'language'. Data flow diagrams and structure charts describe the system in a graphical way and depict the movement of data between modules. A descriptive language such as pseudocode is used for detailing actual operations within the module and will almost certainly be used at some stage in detailed design.

A 'mixed' notation approach is probably the best method for designing IV software. This involves the use of structure charts with program units detailed in pseudocode. The reason for using structure charts goes back to the principles for developing structured software — they complement the technique of stepwise refinement outlined in the previous section.

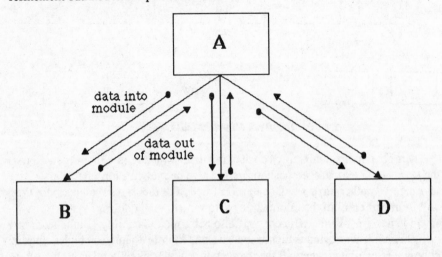

Figure 3 Structure chart

From the process of stepwise refinement, a tree-like diagram is evolved. A structure chart can use this diagram and, by adding directional arrows, depict the flow of data between modules (see Figure 3). This will show the relationship between program units without actually detailing the actual operations.

Pseudocode is the 'lowest level', the most detailed of software design and is best used to describe 'how' a module actually performs its function. Pseudocode is very structured and will use the syntax of a programming language such as Pascal, but be flexible enough to include 'abstract' or informal terms which apply directly to the application for which the software is being developed. In IV there are the customary extensions for the videodisc usage and also for graphics generation. Basically there are no hard and fast rules on what constitutes pseudocode, however, there is need to be consistent and careful when using pseudocode for detailed design.

The above method has been applied to the project in the case study and the one which best suits the authors and their experiences with IV. However, due to the flair and creativity necessary in designing software for IV, from the user specification to the detailed design, there will be variations in how the software engineer utilizes the available design tools. Nevertheless, the end result should be the same — a software design of quality.

IMPLEMENTATION

This is the stage where the software design is transformed into its 'physical' being, either by authoring or a conventional computer programming language. The coding of the system is the most visible expression of the creative work done in design. It is, in fact, the mechanical part of the process. The analysis and design stages provide the platform for the flair and creativity. However, coding can be a labour intensive activity and also a very practical activity which can only be learned by experience. The experience of other IV programmers can be very valuable in providing some guidelines in order to avoid some of the pitfalls. After all, a program will be read more often than its written, so it has to be understandable, especially if the program is to be updated and maintained by someone other than its author. Program readability is not only dependant on the programming or authoring language, it very much lies in the quality of design and the style of writing the code.

This stage involves the use of either an authoring language or system, or an orthodox computer programming language. There is much debate on the pros and cons of each route. The case study highlights a situation where only the programming route could achieve the project aims. Both methods are elaborated in the following sections. The case study highlights a situation where only the programming route could achieve the project aims.

By programming we imply the use of a programming language such as Pascal, 'C', Assembler or even BASIC!

Authoring involves the use of a package, itself coded with one of the above languages, which can develop a software system using relatively simple commands. This route would generally be taken by instructional designers or subject experts who are themselves not computer programmers. The programming option will be employed by professional software developers.

Irrespective of which method is chosen, the preparatory work of analysis and design leading up to the implementation is still vitally important.

Authoring

The concept of authoring is the creation and integration of video images, graphics and text in a relatively simple manner, and applied to a particular problem. In a conventional computer programming environment this would be a difficult task for professional software developers and almost impossible for non-computer literate designers. The reason for the growth in authoring within IV is because instructional designers have taken software development into their own domain. There are benefits to this approach which include the instructional designer having total control over the course development, and also the eliminating of possible communications problems between the instructional and software designers. The overall management of a project may therefore be easier.

Authoring environments in IV usually provide a pre-structured range of facilities and commands which allow an author to construct a training course with relative ease. Included will be functions which permit the creation of specific and important tasks such as graphic screens, menus, question and answer analysis and the control of the input and output devices.

Very few authoring systems are developed solely for IV purposes. They are usually pitched at the wider CBT market and adapted for IV use. Authoring, therefore, is not new and much has been written about the subject. The aim of this section is not to provide a comparison of authoring systems, but rather to set out some criteria for systems and, in general, describe what is involved and the costs. See p00   for the software criteria by which a choice of authoring or programming should be made.

A minimum hardware specification is now generally accepted in IV and is set out in Chapter 2. To ensure compatibility and consistency, authoring systems should should be capable of developing and delivering courses on this specification.

There are generally speaking two types of authoring systems:
- menu-driven
- command-driven

Menu-driven systems, as the name implies, make use of a set of menus from which selections are made. When the system is first invoked a screen will appear containing options such as: create a lesson, execute a lesson, quit the system, and so on. The initial choice will prompt another menu on to the screen with relevant options. At some point there will have to be the typing in of the lesson or module, but it is done within a tight framework.

This is the simplest form of authoring and although mistakes are less common, it can become tedious and restrictive to use.

Command-driven systems are similar to conventional computer languages in that they will have a syntax — that is, they will have a set of commands which may be used and laid out in a specific fashion. These types of systems are more powerful than menu-driven systems, but it takes more time to master the commands. All suppliers of these systems will provide training courses if required. Although simpler than a standard computer language, this system can be used to assemble a prototype very quickly. It could also therefore be used as a communications tool between the instructional designer and the software designer.

Many authoring systems use a mixture of menu-driven and command-driven modes, thus appealing to the novice as well as the more experienced author.

Any authoring system should be relatively simple to use, even for a first timer. It also has to be able to swiftly create simple and complex lessons, or modules, and then edit and execute them interactively.

The following list of authoring systems are probably the most used in IV at the present time:

System	Supplier	Cost
Mentor	Mentor Interactive Training Tel: 0274 307766	£2250
Microtext	Transdata Tel: 01—251 8011	£570
Procal	VPS Interactive Tel: 0273 728686	£1350
Sam	Ferranti Training Systems Tel: 0243 771722	£3000
Tencore	Systems Interactive Tel: 01—994 6477	£2050
Topclass	Format pc Tel: 0773 820011	£390

The above costs are not the end of the investment - there are the additional costs of publishing and licensing. These costs vary considerably between suppliers. If, for example, courses are developed for in-house use only then you may not have to pay anything. If the intention is to sell the course then payment of up to £1500 per course may have to be made to the supplier. There may also be a site licence fee to pay for using the system.

Suppliers provide very good back-up support facilities. This will typically involve manuals, technical assistance, a hotline, maintenance and training. Minimum recommended training requirements are between two and five days and the costs vary from supplier to supplier.

All in all, if authoring is the chosen route for implementation you will have to be very careful in evaluating available systems before purchasing. Every supplier will provide a demo disc and perhaps even customize one to demonstrate the features you have identified as necessary for your proposed IV system.

For an extremely detailed survey of the features and capabilities of the above authoring systems, plus some more, the National Interactive Video Centre or NIVC (tel: 01—387 2233)   have published a report by Gill Strawford titled Authoring Packages — A Comprehensive Report which costs £75.

Programming

An orthodox computer language such as Pascal or 'C' is used to professionally program an IV system. To many, the power and flexibility of a programming language is only answer to the complex requirements of a level three IV training system. In programming there are no pre-structured arrangements pertaining to IV, therefore the language can be manipulated in any way necessary.

By definition, authoring is a dilution of the available computing power within the system. The best way to tap the resources of a most sophisticated hardware set-up is to use the most sophisticated of software, which means programming.

Programming is also more suited to the structured software design techniques outlined earlier in this chapter. Some might say that creativity in design is stifled by structure. This is a complete misconception, at least when applied to software design. The more flexible IV software and the more control put into the hands of the user, the more structured the design has to be. Programming is a very 'exacting' practice — one error may cause the program to crash. Good programming is derived from good design structure.

The major benefit of using a programming language is that there is no compromise. A course can be customized exactly as required without the imposed restrictions of an authoring environment. However (and this is also true of authoring) programming for microcomputers is largely labour intensive and therefore a great deal of responsibility lies with the person(s) developing the software.

One disadvantage of programming is the low productivity rate in comparison to authoring. This is to some extent being redressed, with languages for microcomputers now being developed as packages which include an editor, compiler, interactive debugger plus a host of other utilities which have greatly increased productivity.

Software houses such as Borland and Microsoft produce state-of-the-art packages for software developers which are highly productive and efficient. Also available are off- the-peg utilities such as graphics editors, screen handlers, database handlers and so on. The Turbo Pascal 5.0 environment from Borland will cost less than £100. Add another £150, maximum, for utilities and you have perhaps the most powerful software environment available for a micro.

Another misconception in IV is that authoring is always cheaper than programming. A weaker authoring system can cost ten times as much as a programming environment, and there are no publishing or licence fees with programming. A software engineer will cost more per day than an author. However the overall cost of developing software may be less expensive with a professional software developer. Certainly so if the quality of the final product is included in the equation. There are hidden costs in authoring such as the author's investment in time to learn the system and perhaps also some initial training costs. Currently available, professional software tools should make the experienced IV programmer a highly productive and cost effective person.

On the other hand a good program written in, say, Tencore is better than a badly written program in 'C'. Experience is of vital importance in IV software development. Perhaps the ideal but unrealistic solution would be the provision of powerful enough software tools which could be easily assembled by an instructional designer thus eclipsing the software engineer altogether.

The IBM PS/2 range of microcomputers was launched in April 1987. The architecture of these computers and the use of the Intel 80386 microprocessor will be the hardware trend for the 1990s. It is unlikely that major software applications will be available to take advantage of this raw power before 1991/92, a time lag of 4/5 years. At the time of writing the new operating system OS/2 which is to accompany the PS/2 computers is not fully operational. The existing operating system for micros, the disc operating system (DOS), permits only one user to perform one task on any one machine. OS/2 although still only allowing one user per micro, will permit multitasking. This means that several programs can be run simultaneously and the user can switch between them. This is the type of software which befits a technology such as IV and provides the foundation for highly sophisticated, powerful, exciting and completely new methods for implementing training applications.

The reality at present is that we have the DOS environment to work with for the foreseeable future while software is developed to take advantage of these new developments.

The following section of computer code is a complete program which runs under DOS and also makes use of some of its functions. The program is a utility program which basically transforms the keyboard into a simple remote control keypad. The program could be incorporated into courses or used by someone to peruse a videodisc and catalogue frame numbers. The tools used in the construction of this program were Turbo Pascal 4.0, DOS 3.1 and the MIC—2000 interface software. The MIC—2000 system was chosen because it is the most popular hardware interface between the computer and the videodisc player in the UK and Europe. It also means that the videodisc player is transparent, that is, any player should work with the program, and demonstrates how simple it is to control a videodisc player from a computer programming language.

```
Program Browse(input,output);

        { This program turns the keyboard into a remote control keypad.

          The valid keys are the function keys from F1 to F8, the return and escape keys
          with the plus and minus keys being used from the F4 choice, which is the option to
          step through the videodisc frame by frame.

          No windows or graphics are used to overlay information but a window outlining the
          available keys could be added without any alteration.

          When this program is compiled and run the videodisc will still on frame 10 and
          the system will then be awaiting a key entry. The case statement in the main
          program outlines the valid keys and their function. Any keypress will end each
          individual function.

          The F4 key is the step frame option and after it is pressed you may press the + or
          - keys to move forward or backward and the spacebar to end the option

          The Escape key terminates the program                                           }


uses    crt, dos;                        { turbo pascal libraries                          }

const   startframe = 10;                 { first frame number on videodisc                }
        endframe   54000;                { final frame on videodisc                       }

Var     mic        : text;               { file variable to access MIC system             }
        choice     : word;               { user response                                  }
        audio, index : boolean;          { switch between on/off in audio and index        }
```

```pascal
Procedure InitialiseMIC(var t : text);          { proc to initialise MIC system                 }
Begin
    rewrite(t);                                 { open MIC system for communications            }
    writeln(t,'init');                          { send init command to the MIC system           }
End;


Procedure Read_Key( var key : word);            { proc to read the user's input key             }
Var        regs : registers;                    { Turbo Pascal interface to the 8088            }
                                                { assembly registers                            }
Begin

    regs.ax:=0;                                 { put the input function number in the AX reg.  }
    intr($16,regs);                             { invoke the interrupt which reads the input    }
    key:=regs.ax;                               { put the key input from the keyboard,          }
End;                                            {   in the AX register into a program variable  }

Procedure ScanReverse(var t : text);            { proc to scan backwards and await input        }
Begin
    writeln(t,'play',',',startframe,'/SC');      { command to MIC to begin the scan              }
    writeln(t,'readkey @',',',startframe);        { tell MIC to wait till either a key is pressed }
End;                                            {   or the videodisc scans back to frame 10     }

Procedure FastReverse(var t : text);            { proc to play fastback and and await input     }
Begin
    writeln(t,'play',',',startframe,'/F');       { command to MIC to begin the fast reverse      }
    writeln(t,'readkey @',',',startframe);        { tell MIC to wait till either a key is pressed }
End;                                            {   or the videodisc plays' back to frame 1     }

Procedure PlayReverse(var t : text);            { proc to play backwards and await input        }
Begin
    writeln(t,'play',',',startframe,);           { command to MIC to begin reverse playback      }
    writeln(t,'readkey @',',',startframe);        { tell MIC to wait till either a key is pressed }
End;                                            {   or the videodisc arrives back at frame 1    }

Procedure StepFrame(var t : text);              { proc to step through the disc by still frame  }
Var  disc_step            : word;               { variable to determine which way to step       }
                                                {   through the disc or terminate option        }
Begin
    repeat
      repeat
          read_key(disc_step)                   { call proc to read keyboard entry              }
      until (disc_step = $4E2B) or              { keep repeating keyboard proc until one of     }
            (disc_step = $3920) or              {  three keys are entered:  +  -  spacebar      }
            (disc_step = $4A2D);

      if disc_step = $4E2B
          then writeln(t,'step')                { move forwards if  +  is pressed               }
          else if disc_step=$4A2D
                  then writeln(t,'step /R');     { move backwards if  -  is pressed              }

    until step = $3920;                         { repeat the entire proc until spacebar keyed   }

End;

Procedure PlayFwd(var t : text);                { proc to play disc at normal speed             }
Begin
    writeln(t,'play',',',endframe);              { play from current frame until the end frame   }
    writeln(t,'readkey @',',',endframe);          { play until either a key is pressed or the      }
End;                                            {   last frame is reached                        }

Procedure FastFwd(var t : text);                { proc to play disc at fast forward speed       }
Begin
    writeln(t,'play',',',endframe,'/F');         { fast forward from current frame               }
    writeln(t,'readkey @',',',endframe);          { play until either a key is pressed or the     }
End;                                            {   last frame is reached                        }

Procedure ScanFwd(var t : text);                { proc to play disc at scan forward speed       }
Begin
    writeln(t,'play',',',endframe,'/SC');        { scan from current frame until the end frame   }
    writeln(t,'readkey @',',',endframe);          { scan until either a key is pressed or the     }
End;                                            {   last frame is reached                        }

Procedure Sound(var t : text; var audio_on: boolean);   { proc to toggle the audio on and off    }
Begin
    if (audio_on) then                          { test if the audio is switched on              }
    begin
            writeln(mic,'audio off');           { if it is on then switch it off                }
            audio_on:=false;                    { set the audio test variable to off            }
    end else
    begin
            writeln(mic,'audio on');            { if the audio is off then switch it on         }
            audio-on:=true;                     { set the audio test variable to on             }
    end;
End;
```

```
Procedure PicNum(var t : text; var index_on: boolean);   {prcc to toggle the index on and off            }
Begin
        if (index_on) then                               { test if the index is switched on             ;
        begin
                writeln(mic,'index off');                { if it is on then switch it off               }
                index_on:=false;                         { set the index test variable to off           }
        end  else
        begin
                writeln(mic,'index on');                 {if the index is off then switch it on          }
                audio-on:=true;                          { set the audio test variable to on            } /
        end;
End;

Begin { the actual program }
        assign(mic,'MIC');                               { assign the MIC Device Driver to a variable.   }
                                                         { The MIC DD must be in the local directory     }
        initialiseMIC(mic);                              { initialise the MIC DD to default states       }
        writeln(mic,'video on');                         { switch the video on                           }
        writeln(mic,'audio on');                         { switch the audio on                           }
        writeln(mic,'index on');                         { switch the index on                           }
        writeln(mic,'still 10');                         { still the videodisc player at frame 10        }
        audio:=true;                                     { set the audio variable to be on               }
        index:=true;                                     { set the index variable to be on               }
        choice:=0;                                       { initialise the user's input to have zero      }
        repeat
                read_key(choice);                        { call proc to read user's request              }
                case choice of                           { depending upon entry do one of the following  }
                $3B00  : ScanReverse(mic);               { - F1 - call scan reverse proc.               }
                $3C00  : Fast Reverse(mic);              { - F2 - call fast reverse proc.               }
                $3D00  : PlayReverse(mic);               { - F3 - call normal play reverse proc.        }
                $3E00  : StepFrame(mic);                 { - F4 - call step frame proc.                 }
                $3F00  : PlayFwd(mic);                   { - F5 - call normal play forward proc.        }
                $4000  : FastFwd(mic);                   { - F6 - call fast play proc.                  }
                $4100  : ScanFwd(mic);                   { - F7 - call scan forward proc.               }
                $4200  : PicNum(mic,index);              { - F8 - call index proc.                      }
                $1C0D  : Sound(mic,audio);               { - RETURN - call audio proc.                  }
                $11B   : {Escape is chosen}              { - ESC - request to terminate program         }
                else  choice:=$4200;                     { if none of above keys pressed then give any   }
                end;                                     {     valid key so as not to cause an error     }
                writeln(mic,'still');                    { still the player at the end of each chrice    }
        until choice = $11B;                             { start again at repeat unless exit required    }
        writeln(mic,'video off');                        { after escape pressed switch off the video     }
        writeln(mic,'audio off');                        { and then switch off the audio                 }
        close(mic);                                      { close communications with the MIC DD          }
End.                                                     { end of program                               }
```

Figure 4 A Program!

Choice Factors

There is no doubt that the quality of the software tools used in the construction of an IV system has a considerable bearing on the end result. Often software designers or project managers are confronted with the problem of choosing between authoring and programming. The problem continues when a further choice has to be made between the different systems and languages. There are, unfortunately, cases where software has been decided upon without prior consultation with the software engineer. If at all possible this should be avoided since anyone developing software has to be familiar with the development tools.

There are four general criteria for suitability in software development which can be applied to both authoring or programming:

(1) Systems or languages must be in use in IV. The features should be well documented and the environment should provide the facilities for construction, execution and testing of software.

(2) The completed software should be portable and hardware independent. Standard software tools should be used, such as device drivers, in order to ensure the transparency of the hardware components.

(3) The system must be applicable to the applications problem - the Cobol

programming language, for example, may not be useful for external communications and high speed screen updates. Similarly, if all you need is set of multiple choice questions then authoring may be the best route.

(4) The language/system should support the structured design techniques of software engineering. IV is a complex arena for software design and the techniques of software engineering reduce the complexity of design.

The overall aim of any IV software system is maximum performance for the application in question. If the application is for point of information or point of sale purposes then perhaps the 'gloss' on the system is more important than the performance of the software. For evaluating the software needs in training situations the best option may be to start with the premise that an authoring system will be used. Key elements of the system are identified and matched against the ability of the authoring system. Areas where performance may be of major importance include:

- screen handling
- complex graphics
- user interface
- answer analysis
- large information structure handling
- input/output operations
- external file manipulation
- peripheral device control
- mathematical operations
- direct memory access
- response times
- execution speed.

If some of the above list is critical to the success of the system, it may be desirable to use a programming language for maximum effect. Alternatively, it might very be that an authoring system can cope with 90 per cent of the requirements and programming is necessary for the other 10 per cent where performance is critical. Most authoring system will allow this 'mixed' approach and can be of some benefit, but it does make software development more difficult. The actual interface between the authoring system and the programming language can also be cumbersome and the speed of the system may be affected during this link time.

TESTING THE SOLUTION

Anyone who has created a program, either by using an authoring system or a programming language, will recognize the importance of, and necessity for testing. It is highly unlikely that a program written for IV will work completely at the first attempt. Testing is an essential process in order to verify the software.

Testing is an ongoing process beginning at the design stage, however in many cases testing the system tends to be carried out immediately prior to the software being released. Sometimes the trialling of systems is used to test the system. This should not be done — trialling is used more to evaluate the working system rather than find errors within a partially tested system.

By testing we do not mean the automatic checking of the program statements. Errors in the construction and use of the authoring or programming language for a particular application will be picked up and pointed out to the developer by the system. A good authoring system or programming language will inform the developer of the location and type of error. These errors are relatively easy to clear up. Testing is the process of identifying errors within a program.

There are two other types of errors, run-time and logical, which are more problematical and to which testing is addressed. Run-time errors cause a program to crash during execution. There are many reasons for this type of error including erroneous input data or a badly devised arithmetic calculation. As with syntax errors a good system will help in locating the offending statement. Logical errors are the most difficult to detect. These occur when the program seems to work correctly but produces the wrong results on execution. A software developer has to then rely on the quality of the design and testing in order to locate and correct the error.

Program testing demonstrates the presence of these errors. It does not demonstrate their absence. Even the most stringent of testing strategies cannot guarantee an error free program.

Debugging is often thought to be the same as testing. Although closely related, each has a distinct role. Testing is the process of finding errors in a program, while debugging is the process of locating and correcting them.

Testing the code involves the formulation of a test plan. This test plan must reflect the fundamental principles of testing, namely:

(1)   the objective is to uncover errors
(2)   this should be carried out in a systematic way
(3)   testing should begin at the design stage
(4)   the results should be recorded.

Program testing is destructive by nature. The aim is to cause the program to behave in a manner not intended by the author of the program. An advantage of having the author of the program produce and execute a test plan is that he or she will have in depth knowledge of the structure of the program and be able to validate such things as:

- data structures
- answer analysis conditions
- branching conditions
- initialization and content of variables
- parameter passing.

Whenever possible, testing should begin in the design stages and certainly before the software system is put together. This can only happen if the authoring system or programming language allows you to compile and run individual modules.

When someone develops a program there is a natural affinity between the author and the program. There is no real desire to 'crash' the program. Because of this, the creator prefers to prove the program works. Unfortunately this is not adequate for demonstrating the presence of errors.

Adversarial testing by someone other than the author is necessary for full validation of the program. This objective test plan should only be carried out after the subjective testing has been completed by the author.

Test Strategies

A complete test plan strategy will include the use of 'white-box' and 'black-box' testing. White-box testing should be carried out by the author as there is a requirement to understand the design and coding of the system. This type of testing views the system as a set of individual modules and the aim is to examine the program's internal structure. In IV this subjective testing could be a major undertaking. Test data is constructed and a systematic plan is detailed in order that:

(1)   All statements within a module are executed at least once.

(2)   Correct parameters are being passed between modules.

(3)   Answer analysis functions are examined in detail.

(4)   All loops are executed the minimum and maximum number of iterations.

(5)   Internal data structures are exercised to ensure boundaries and content.

(6)   All conditional decisions are exercised.

(7)   All possible inputs and possible outputs are correct and in the proper format.

(8)   All peripheral devices used are utilized.

(9)   All test results are archived.

The basis of a white-box test plan will be a set of program paths which should execute every statement. A good method for assessing your understanding of a program is to introduce known errors into the code and see if the behaviour of the program is what you expect.

If testing has not been possible on individual units, then this test plan will be all the more complex as the author attempts to examine every module within the complete program.

In black-box testing the system is viewed as a complete entity and all the functions of the program are tested. The overall behaviour of the program is checked and, for IV systems, the best person to perform these tests is someone who is familiar with the functional specification but has not been involved in the design and coding of software. Understanding what the system is supposed to do, the person performing the test can construct test data to examine the general facets of the system and uncover errors such as:

-   incorrect or missing features

-   incorrect answer analysis

-   user interface errors

-   incorrect handling of exceptional data

-   performance errors, such as bad synchronization of video and graphics.

This test data should be constructed so that every possible route through the program is traced. Invalid data as well as valid data is used as input to the system.

These two testing strategies are not alternatives - they are complementary to one another. White-box testing is performed first, followed by black-box testing. This is a very creative stage in the software development lifecycle and has an important part to play in the quality of the finished product.

SOFTWARE QUALITY

The subject of quality assurance within the software development process is acknowledged but is given scant regard in practice.

The achievement of quality is a prolonged process and is not confined to the final listing of the computer code. Quality assessment begins at the highest specification stage, and carries on through testing and involves everyone connected with the project, including the end user.

Each stage of the lifecycle process should have its outcomes demonstrated as being of acceptable quality. Major quality issues should be raised at the following stages:
- functional specification
- design
- coding
- testing
- documentation

The functional specification (see pp 143-144) is a crucial document and a checklist should be drawn up to ensure that all the issues are addressed and that the document correctly 'implements' the user requirements specification. At this stage it is also possible to 'walk-through' or hand-trace the system to ensure that there are no obvious errors or omissions.

The quality review documents have a knock on effect in that, for example, the previous reviews at functional and design stages will act as a measure throughout the actual coding of the system and will therefore improve the quality of the final code. The entire process of quality assurance begins at the outset of a project and is interlinked until the project ends.

The final code is no doubt important, for which good programming is crucial. For the production of quality code the following criteria have to be met:
- Accurate — the program works as intended
- Reliable — ..and does it consistently
- Robustness — can handle exceptional data
- Efficiency — has speed and resource performance
- Ease of Use — simple interface, good documentation
- Structured — module layout, no redundant code
- Readable — meaningful names and comments
- Maintainable — good structure, easily amended

If the instructional design is of a high quality, and if the implementation, after the testing of the software, contains the above features, then there should exist a quality IV software system.

Documentation

Documentation is the information about a program available in writing. It's not one of the most exciting tasks in software development, but it is an essential one. For the users this will be their firstencounter with the system, and for those who are to maintain and update the system, the quality of the software documentation is very important.

There are two main groups of people who need to be provided with the documentation: end users and the company or individual who will maintain the software system. Both need documentation for different purposes: one to operate the system, the other to understand its construction. All documents produced during the software development are part of the documentation, especially key documents such as the user specification, functional specification, coding design document and the test plan document with the results.

System documentation is used for maintenance purposes and contains all the documents which are necessary to alter the program code with ease and without side-effects. Typical documents include:

- user requirement specification
- functional specification
- all software design documents
- test plan and results
- program source code
- installation procedure
- all files associated with the program
- technical issues such as equipment, memory requirements, details of the software development environment.

The above list should provide a comprehensive view of the system thus cutting down on maintenance time.

The best known piece of documentation is the user manual. This is where the user gains a first impression of the system, so the material in this document has to be carefully prepared. IV is a new technology and therefore many people will feel uneasy at the prospect of using it. The user documentation should instil confidence in the user and be very thorough in its explanations. This should to be done without the use of jargon.

There is the problem of who actually writes the user manual. In professional computing a technical author may be used. However in IV an instructio1al designer should be able to perform this task with help and reference coming from the the software designer.

There should be no need to read a complete manual before using the system. An introductory section should put the learner in an 'interactive' situation by the use of tutorials and examples. A typical route through the package should be demonstrated which incorporates all the general features. There is no need to describe the technical wizardry behind the overlaying of graphics on the video or any other such technical features.

The introduction must also demonstrate what happens when mistakes are made and how to take corrective action. This is important to build confidence in the user but is often overlooked in user documentation. The user manual, then, should include instructions covering the following:

- The installation procedure and any information on customising thesystem for different hardware
- An introductory section outlined above
- Description of the objectives of the system
- A detailed reference section where all routes and features are detailed
- Error messages and corrective action
- Comprehensive index
- Information to enable users to contact the organisation(s) responsible for after sales service and maintenance.

As with any user guide the information should be clearly laid out and easy to understand, with no superfluous data. The nature of IV means that there will be a good deal of interaction with the system, and therefore a large amount of operational detail. Care should be taken so as to not to engulf the user in a morass of technical detail.

CASE STUDY: THE NORTH WEST EDUCATIONAL COMPUTING PROJECT

A general introduction to the North West Educational Computing Project (NWECP) along with its broad aims are set out in Chapter 4. Basically, interactive video was deemed to be a potential vehicle for the application of teaching foreign languages and the project team was to explore the possibilities. The project team consisted of three core members who were professionals in the fields of computing, foreign language teaching and project administration.

No member of the project team had any previous experience of the technology involved in IV. However at the very outset of the project we decided that the project would not be 'technology-led'. The subject field, language teaching, was the impetus to design and develop the applications system which was in effect the combined hardware and software systems.

Our main thrust therefore, from a technical stance, was to assemble a suitable hardware configuration and develop software which would control the hardware and correctly implement the instructional design from the languages specialist. The project plar included time for research and feasibility.

Hardware assembly

In the initial stages of the project we experimented with the then state-of-the-art configuration consisting of: IBM PCXT, Philips 835 laservision and a Cameron touch screen.

As the project brief was to develop a system for the correct application of the instructional design there was scope for altering the system. This flexibility in hardware specification was to prove valuable in the light of technological developments relating to IV. Of the original assembly, only the IBM PCXT was used in the final delivery system. In fact the final assembly did not become a reality until the last quarter of the project. The design of the system allowed for the adoption technical advances in hardware. If this had not been possible we might not have successfully implemented the system to the standard demanded by the applications area.

One person was responsible for hardware and software. This single-author approach had the benefit of one person grappling with the intricacies of the hardware and then using this knowledge for the development of software tools to exploit the technology to the fullest.

The final IV configuration on which the course was delivered consisted of an IBM PCXT, Philips 831 laservision player, Sony KX14CP1 monitor and the MIC —2000 interface. We used the newly released MIC —2000 system which had become available towards the latter half of the project.

The standard way in which the MIC —2000 system communicated with the videodisc player meant that integrating the MIC —2000 software into our developing software was relatively straightforward. In fact the MIC system has been our 'insurance policy' against technological developments rendering our system obsolete. Its open architecture approach to hardware and software meant that we could embrace the latest developments in IV technology at minimum cost. Since the conclusion of the project we have successfully transported the system to the new videodisc players from Sony and Philips, to the new IBM PS/2 microcomputer (including compatibles) and also to a range of different monitors. All this has been done with an absolute minimum of software alteration.

Perhaps the most important factor in the hardware assembly was that we never tied ourselves to one hardware supplier. This allowed for the integration of technological advances and resulted in a flexible delivery system capable of using a different computer, different videodisc player and different monitors if necessary.

The Two Templates

From the instructional design there came two specifications. These were termed Template 1 and Template 2. The first for beginners, and the second for intermediate learners.

The first course to be specified was Template 1 which used available videodisc material for which software was designed and produced to implement the instructional design in the best possible way. The footage available on the videodisc was not ideal. Basically a linear programme had been taken and pressed to videodisc. The footage was therefore not subject to the rigorous demands of synchronization between sound and vision required for IV. For language learning the utterances have to be preciously segmented and the speaker should be on screen for the duration of that utterance.

The Template 2 specification took on board much of the lessons learned from Template 1 and, as a result, video material was shot specifically for the project. Also the reaction from Template 1 indicated that the users enjoyed the freedom afforded by IV to exploit both the visual movement and the written word. The aim of the software for Template 2 was to make the system as flexible as possible by putting as much control as possible into the hands of the user. There is a definite correlation between the ease of use, and user control over the system, and the complexity of software.

Software Development

This overall software philosophy was to help in the production of a user specification and then develop a functional solution for both templates.

In Template 1 the languages specialist was responsible for the production of the user requirements specification. The basic requirement for Template 1 was to transfer a known teaching methodology into an IV system. The software designer basically gave advice on what would not be possible with the technology.

The ideas generated for Template 2, however, were much more ambitious. In this case the software designer played a more prominent role in the user specification although, as in Template 1, the document was drawn up in the first instance by the instructional designer. By this stage, the team members had an appreciation of each other's tasks and a method of communications, so vital in a project, began to evolve. The software designer began to understand the language teaching aims and the instructional designer had an appreciation of what a computer was capable of doing both as a stand alone and also in unison with the videodisc player.

Design Criteria

It was very important that certain 'rules' for designing the software were identified early on. The basic criteria applied to the templates were a consequence of the central goal - to minimize the complexity of the system and put maximum flexibility under learner control.

It was decided that there would be three ground rules which would apply to software design throughout the project:
  (1) Dividing the system into language activities which could be developed independently from the system.
  (2) Moving between activities should be interpreted as the learner changing options and information passed kept to a minimum.
  (3) The modules should be as small as possible.

The above criteria did not dictate the design process, rather it enriched the design by providing a yardstick to the overall design direction.

In practice the two templates evolved in very different ways. Template 1 was very structured in educational terms. The development of the software was not as structured as it might have been as there was a lot of experimentation during the design and implementation stages which resulted in informal and casual additions being made as late as the testing stage.

Template 2 was very different in that it was less structured in educational terms and much more ambitious. This meant that the design process had to be far more thorough and precise. The result was a much more flexible system from the user's point of view but a highly structured implementation in terms of computer code.

Detailed Template Design

The user requirements specification for both templates was an extensive piece of work, mainly involving the foreign language specialist supported by the software specialist. The functional specification, on the other hand, was the responsibility of the software specialist with the language specialist playing the supporting role.

After the type of information which was to be input, analysed and output from the system was determined, it was necessary to determine how best to implement the data structures. There was a lot of text manipulation and it was decided that there should be a number of major structures with external files containing statistical information to manipulate the structure and its contents in the desired fashion.

In both templates the method adopted for setting out the software design was structure charts and a type of pseudocode, usable for IV purposes. Many charts were developed as the system began to take shape and it soon became apparent that there was a need for a module which contained only utility procedures to be accessed by other modules. Typical utility procedures included some for screen operations, keyboard handling and formatting of input and output.

The first chart to be developed was one which reflected the user specification, summarized in Chapter Four. This was the case for both Template 1 and Template 2.

This was the 'highest level' of the system and provided the basis for further decomposition of the system. In fact, the viewing section was the 'root' for a chart which spanned three A4 pages. The modules became simpler and well defined the further 'down' the structure chart they appeared.

The development of the structure charts was a rigorous and demanding activity. Applying the data structures and depicting the movement of information between the modules is not at all simple. Attention to detail at this stage paid dividends when it came to actually coding the system. Apart from taking less time to code, there was also an appreciable reduction in the estimated time for testing and debugging.

Once it was perceived that the system existed in chart form, pseudocode was used to precisely detail and structure the design in such a way that it could then be directly coded using the chosen computer programming languages. What happened in practice was that the pseudocode implementation threw up some omissions and errors which resulted in the charts being modified.

The pseudocode notation was highly specific to IV. We used visual diagrams to indicate the usage of the videodisc and descriptive English, which was really a mixture of computer and IV jargon and paraphrased English, to detail operations.

The entire design process provided a great deal of information which was extremely useful. These documents were developed in a structured manner and to the software specialist acted as a complete 'reference manual', and also as a quality review document, during the implementation stage.

The Final Implementation

After some investigation it became clear that authoring systems were unsuitable for the project's implementation phase. They were deemed unsuitable for a number of reasons. Ignoring the lack of graphics and computational facilities, it was impossible to use a software system which had no complex data structure handling, cumbersome file input and output and a relatively slow execution speed. There was also an inability to directly access the features of the computer such as screen memory and necessary features of the operating system. Generally authoring systems, or languages, are not very well structured in computer terms, and therefore incompatible with a structured design approach for software development.

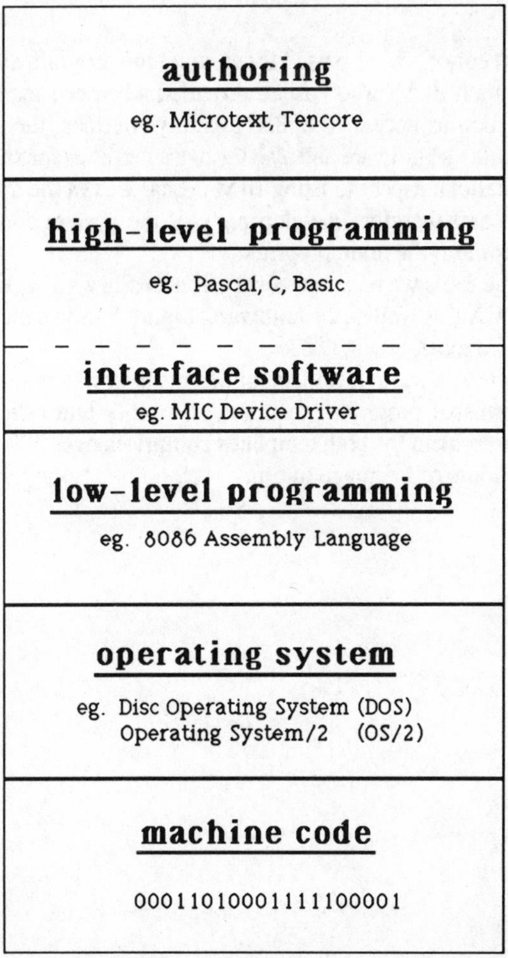

```
┌─────────────────────────────────────┐
│            authoring                 │
│       eg. Microtext, Tencore         │
├─────────────────────────────────────┤
│      high-level programming          │
│        eg.  Pascal, C, Basic         │
│ ─ ─ ─ ─ ─ ─ ─ ─ ─ ─ ─ ─ ─ ─ ─ ─ ─ ─ │
│        interface software            │
│        eg. MIC Device Driver         │
├─────────────────────────────────────┤
│       low-level programming          │
│      eg. 8086 Assembly Language      │
├─────────────────────────────────────┤
│         operating system             │
│   eg. Disc Operating System (DOS)    │
│       Operating System/2   (OS/2)    │
├─────────────────────────────────────┤
│          machine code                │
│      000110100011111100001           │
└─────────────────────────────────────┘
```

Figure 6 Computer software levels

Speed, flexibility, efficiency and precise control over the system were crucial when considering the implementation. To achieve the versatility required for a foreign language learning system some work was carried out to ascertain which software tools were best suited to the developing system. The tools used in the programming were:

- IBM Pascal — a more powerful version of standard Pascal.
- 8088 Assembler — native language of the Intel 8088 microprocessor.
- Disk Operating System — the operating system of the IBM PCXT (DOS 2.1).
- Basic I/O System — the machine code routines in ROM on the PCXT.
- MIC Device Driver — supporting software to standardise videodisc access.

A standard text editor was also used for creating the program and associated files.

IBM Pascal, much like Turbo Pascal, provided advanced facilities not found in standard Pascal such as access to 8088 assembly routines, the software interrupt system, the computer's hardware and also the extra facilities for string manipulation. Another very beneficial aspect to using IBM Pascal was in the ability to separately compile modules and therefore develop parts of the system and test them before incorporating them into the main program.

Using the above tools we now had access, if necessary, to each layer of software within the IBM PCXT as well as the hardware. Figure 5 shows the layered organisation of the software tools.

This approach to software development has resulted in a number of advantages, particularly in terms of program execution, flexibility and efficiency. In all the complete software system for both templates comprises over 200 files and provides in excess of 100 hours of language tuition — all on one floppy disc.

FURTHER READING LIST

Bayard-White, C.(1987) *An Introduction to Interactive Video*, National Interactive Video Centre and Council for Educational Technology

Droar, Tony (ed.) *Computer Controlled Interactive Video multi-media authoring systems*

Interact '87 (1987) *Conference Proceedings* PLF Communciations

Laurillard, D.(ed.) (1987) *Interactive Media* Ellis Horwood, Chichester

Miller, Charles R. (1987) *Essential Guide to Interactive Videodisc Hardware and Applications*, Meckler

Parsloe, E (ed) (1983)*Interactive Video*, Sigma Technical Press

Philips International — J.M.Preston (1987/1988) *Compact Disc Interactive — A Designer's Overview* Kluwer Technical Books, Deventer — Antwerpen

Strawford, G (1988) *Authoring Packages A Comparative Report* National Interactive Video Centre

Telemedia GmbH (1988) *Applications List*

INDEX